PRIMARY
comprehension

Fiction and nonfiction texts

Science Fiction

Poetry

Mystery

Myth/Legend

Fable

Play

Adventure

Fantasy

Fairytale

Horror/Supernatural

Humorous

Published by Prim-Ed Publishing
www.prim-ed.com

6259C

PRIMARY COMPREHENSION (Book G)

Published by Prim-Ed Publishing 2006
Reprinted under licence by Prim-Ed Publishing 2006
Copyright© R.I.C. Publications® 2005
ISBN 1 84654 014 3
PR–6259

Additional titles available in this series:
PRIMARY COMPREHENSION (Book A)
PRIMARY COMPREHENSION (Book B)
PRIMARY COMPREHENSION (Book C)
PRIMARY COMPREHENSION (Book D)
PRIMARY COMPREHENSION (Book E)
PRIMARY COMPREHENSION (Book F)

Internet websites

In some cases, websites or specific URLs may be recommended. While these are checked and rechecked at the time of publication, the publisher has no control over any subsequent changes which may be made to webpages. It is *strongly* recommended that the class teacher checks *all* URLs before allowing students to access them.

View all pages online

Website: www.prim-ed.com
Email: sales@prim-ed.com

PRIMARY COMPREHENSION

Foreword

Primary comprehension is a series of seven books designed to provide opportunities for pupils to read texts in a variety of fiction, poetry and nonfiction genres, to answer questions at literal, deductive and evaluative levels and to practise a variety of selected comprehension strategies.

Titles in this series include:

- *Primary Comprehension* Book A
- *Primary Comprehension* Book B
- *Primary Comprehension* Book C
- *Primary Comprehension* Book D
- *Primary Comprehension* Book E
- *Primary Comprehension* Book F
- *Primary Comprehension* Book G

Contents

TEACHERS NOTES

Twenty different texts from a variety of genres are given. These include humour, fantasy, a diary, a myth/legend, folktale, mystery, adventure, horror/supernatural, fairytale, play, fable, science fiction, poetry and informational texts/nonfiction such as a journal, a timetable, letter, report, biography, journalistic writing and autobiography.

Three levels of questions are used to indicate the reader's comprehension of each text.

One or more particular comprehension strategies has been chosen for practice with each text.

Each text is given over pages. Each group of four pages consists of:

~ a teachers page

~ pupil page – 1   (which always includes the text and sometimes literal questions)

~ pupil page – 2   (which gives literal, deductive and evaluative questions)

~ pupil page – 3   (which concentrates on the chosen comprehension strategy/ strategies)

Teachers page

The **title of the text** is given.

The particular **genre** is given.

Question types and comprehension strategies refer to the three levels of questioning and any particular strategies used.

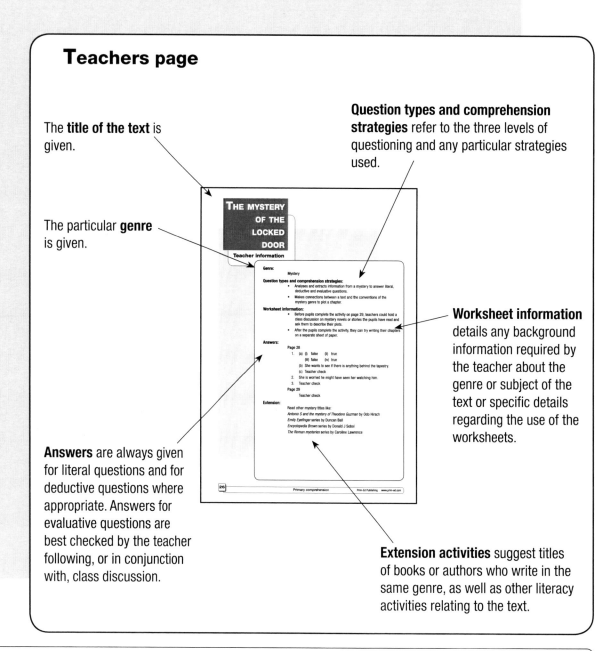

Worksheet information details any background information required by the teacher about the genre or subject of the text or specific details regarding the use of the worksheets.

Answers are always given for literal questions and for deductive questions where appropriate. Answers for evaluative questions are best checked by the teacher following, or in conjunction with, class discussion.

Extension activities suggest titles of books or authors who write in the same genre, as well as other literacy activities relating to the text.

TEACHERS NOTES

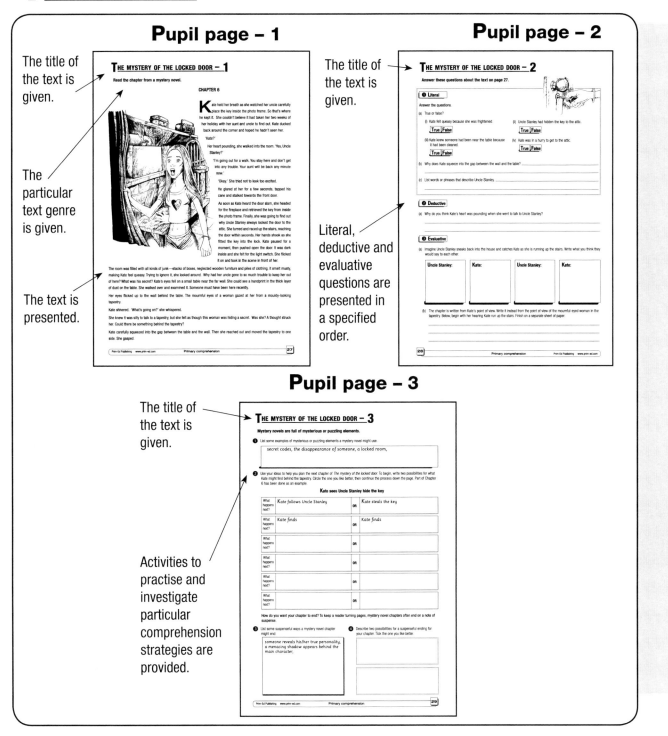

Pupil page – 1

The title of the text is given.

The particular text genre is given.

The text is presented.

Pupil page – 2

The title of the text is given.

Literal, deductive and evaluative questions are presented in a specified order.

Pupil page – 3

The title of the text is given.

Activities to practise and investigate particular comprehension strategies are provided.

Types of questions

Pupils are given **three types (or levels) of questions** to assess their comprehension of a particular text in each genre:

- **Literal questions** are those which can be found directly in the text. These come first in the questions and are grouped.
- **Deductive (or inferential) questions** follow the literal questions. Deductive questions are implied in the text and require the reader to read between the lines and think a bit more deeply about what has just been read.
- **Evaluative (or response/applied) questions** require the reader to think even further about the text and incorporate his/her personal experiences and knowledge to answer.

Answers for literal questions are always given and may be found on the teachers page. Answers for deductive questions are given where appropriate. Evaluative questions are best checked by the teacher following, or in conjunction with, class discussion.

TEACHERS NOTES

Comprehension strategies

Reading comprehension is an essential part of the reading process. Pupils need to comprehend what they read in order to become fluent readers.

The teacher is crucial in teaching and encouraging the use of comprehension strategies. Pupils' comprehension improves when teachers provide explicit instruction in comprehension strategies and when they implement activities that provide opportunities to practise and understand these strategies.

Several specific comprehension strategies have been selected for practice in this book.

Although specific examples have been selected, often other strategies, such as scanning, are used in conjunction with those indicated, even though they may not be stated. Rarely does a reader use a single strategy to comprehend a text.

Strategy definitions

Predicting	Prediction involves the pupil using illustrations, text or background knowledge to help them construct meaning. Pupils might predict what texts could be about, what could happen or how characters could act or react. Prediction may occur before, during and after reading, and can be adjusted during reading.
	Pages 2–5, 6–9, 10–13, 14–17 and 30–33 use the strategy of predicting.
Making connections	Pupils comprehend texts by linking their prior knowledge and the new information given in the text. Pupils may make connections between the text and themselves, between the new text and other texts previously read, and between the text and the world.
	Pages 6–9, 10–13, 14–17, 18–21, 22–25, 26–29, 30–33, 34–37, 38–41, 42–45 and 46–49 use the strategy of making connections.
Comparing	This strategy is closely linked to the strategy of making connections. Pupils make comparisons by thinking more specifically about the similarities and differences between the connections being made.
	Pages 18–21, 34–37, 38–41, 42–45 and 46–49 use the strategy of comparing.
Sensory imaging	Sensory imaging involves pupils utilising all five senses to create mental images of passages in the text. Pupils use visual, auditory, olfactory, kinaesthetic or emotional images as well as their personal experiences to create these images. The images may help them to make predictions, form conclusions, interpret information and remember details.
	Pages 10–13, 30–33 and 50–53 use the strategy of sensory imaging.
Determining importance	The strategy of determining importance is particularly helpful when pupils are trying to comprehend informational texts. It involves pupils determining the important theme or main idea of particular paragraphs or passages.
	As pupils become effective readers, they will constantly ask themselves what is most important in a phrase, sentence, paragraph, chapter or whole text. To determine importance, pupils will need to use a variety of information, such as the purpose for reading, their knowledge of the topic, background experiences and beliefs, and understanding of the text format.
	Pages 22–25, 34–37, 54–57, 58–61 and 62–65 use the strategy of determining importance.

TEACHERS NOTES

Strategy definitions

Skimming Skimming is the strategy of looking quickly through texts to gain a general impression or overview of the content. Readers often use this strategy to quickly assess whether a text, or part of it, will meet their purpose. Because this book deals predominantly with comprehension *after* reading, skimming has not been included as one of the major strategies.

Scanning Scanning is the strategy of quickly locating specific details such as dates, places or names, or those parts of the text which support a particular point of view. Scanning is often used but not specifically mentioned when used in conjunction with other strategies.

Pages 58–61, 66–69 and 70–73 use the strategy of scanning.

Synthesising Synthesising is the strategy which enables pupils to collate a range of information from a variety of sources in order to comprehend text. Pupils recall information, order details and piece information together to make sense of the text. Synthesising helps pupils to continually monitor their understanding of the text. Synthesising involves connecting, comparing, determining importance, posing questions and creating images.

Pages 70–73 and 74–77 use the strategy of synthesising.

Paraphrasing/Summarising Summarising involves the processes of recording key ideas, main points or the most important information from a text. Summarising or paraphrasing reduces a larger piece of text to the most important details.

Pages 62–65, 66–69 and 78–81 use the strategy of summarising/paraphrasing.

Shared and guided reading

Reading comprehension needs to be taught if pupils are to learn how to understand and engage with texts. The structure of comprehension lessons needs to provide direct teaching on the application of reading comprehension strategies.

Shared reading To introduce the lesson, the teacher models reading the text, including a demonstration of how to use the comprehension strategies required by the specific unit of work. The demonstration might include:
- linking information in new text to prior knowledge
- generating mental images of parts of text
- asking 'why' questions
- pausing during reading and asking predictive questions
  or any of the strategies outlined on pages vi and vii.

Guided reading The pupils work in groups to complete the comprehension activities. The teacher works with and supports the pupils, prompting them to use different strategies to solve the questions; for example, the strategy modelled in the shared reading session should be applied to the text.

Plenary Comprehension lessons should be concluded using a plenary session, giving the teacher and pupils the opportunity to discuss a range of issues, including:
- re-emphasis and practise of strategies
- clarification of misconceptions
- reflection and personal response
- explanation of how pupils solved particular questions
- presentation and discussion of work

TEACHERS NOTES

Genre definitions

Fiction and poetry

Science fiction

These stories include backgrounds or plots based upon possible technology or inventions, experimental medicine, life in the future, environments drastically changed, alien races, space travel, gene engineering, dimensional portals or changed scientific principles. Science fiction encourages readers to suspend some of their disbelief and examine alternate possibilities.

Horror/Supernatural

Stories of this type aim to make the reader feel fear, disgust or horror. A number of horror stories have become classics. These include *Frankenstein* by Mary Shelley, *Dracula* by Bram Stoker and *Dr Jekyll and Mr Hyde* by Robert Louis Stevenson.

Mystery stories

Stories of this kind focus on suspense and the solving of a mystery. Plots of mysteries often revolve around a crime, such as murder, theft or kidnapping. The hero must solve the mystery, overcoming unusual events, threats, assaults and often unknown forces or enemies. Stories about detectives, police, private investigators, amateur sleuths, spies, thrillers and courtroom dramas usually fall into this genre.

Fables

A fable is a short story which states a moral. Fables often use talking animals or animated objects as the main characters. The interaction of the animals or animated objects reveals general truths about human nature.

Fairytales

These tales are usually about elves, dragons, hobgoblins, sprites or magical beings and are often set in the distant past. Fairytales usually begin with the phrase 'Once upon a time ...' and end with the words ' ... and they lived happily ever after'. Charms, disguises and talking animals may also appear in fairytales.

Fantasy

A fantasy may be any text or story which is removed from reality. Stories may be set in nonexistent worlds such as an elf kingdom, on another planet or in alternate versions of the known world. The characters may not be human (dragons, trolls etc.) or may be humans who interact with non-human characters.

Folktales

Stories which have been passed from one generation to the next by word of mouth rather than being written down are folktales. Folktales may include sayings, superstitions, social rituals, legends or lore about the weather, animals or plants.

Plays

Plays are specific pieces of drama, usually enacted on a stage by a number of actors dressed in make-up and appropriate costumes.

Adventure stories

Exciting events and actions feature in these stories. Character development, themes or symbolism are not as important as the actions or events in an adventure story.

Humour

Humour involves characters or events which promote laughter, pleasure or humour in the reader.

Poetry

This is a genre which utilises rhythmic patterns of language. The patterns include meter (high and low stressed syllables), syllabification (the number of syllables in each line), rhyme, alliteration, or a combination of these. Poems often use figurative language.

Myths

These are stories which explain a belief, practice or natural phenomenon and usually involve gods, demons or supernatural beings. A myth does not necessarily have a basis in fact or a natural explanation.

Legends

Legends are told as though the events were actual historical events. Legends may or may not be based on an elaborated version of an historical event. Legends are usually about human beings, although gods may intervene in some way throughout the story.

TEACHERS NOTES

Genre definitions

Nonfiction

Journalistic writing
Usually formal and structured, journalistic writing aims to present information accurately, clearly and efficiently rather than to present and develop an individual writer's style. Journalistic writing is usually written in the third person.

Letters
These are written conversations sent from one person to another. Letters usually begin with a greeting, contain the information to be related and conclude with a farewell signed by the sender.

Reports
Reports are written documents describing the findings of an individual or group. They may take the form of a newspaper report, sports or police report, or a report about an animal, person or object.

Biographies
An account of a person's life written by another person is a biography. The biography may be about the life of a celebrity or an historical figure.

Autobiography
An autobiography is a piece of writing in which a writer uses his/her own life as the basis for a biography.

Journals
A journal is a continued series of texts written by a person about his/her life experiences and events. Journals may include descriptions of daily events as well as thoughts and emotions.

Diaries
A diary contains a description of daily events in a person's life.

Other **informational texts** such as **timetables** are excellent sources to teach and assess comprehension skills. Others may include **diagrams, graphs, advertisements, maps, plans, tables, charts, lists, posters** and **programmes**.

CURRICULUM LINKS

England Literacy
Year 6 Extension

Texts

Objectives	Elf boy meets Superman® (2–5)	Between outer-earth and inner-earth (6–9)	Lucky Jim (10–13)	Amazing Amy! (14–17)	Krishna and the serpent (18–21)	The children of Lir (22–25)	The mystery of the locked door (26–29)	The rescue (30–33)	Goody Two Shoes (34–37)	School timetable (38–41)	Two letters (42–45)	Hex and the captive city of Hur (46–49)	The secret book (50–53)	Don't count your chickens! (54–57)	Irish legends (58–61)	A surfing champion (62–65)	Bare trees baffle local farmer (66–69)	Mirror image (70–73)	Life of a convict (74–77)	My bass guitar and my computer (78–81)
Term 1																				
Read a range of fiction and poetry:																				
– classic fiction					●	●								●						
Read a range of nonfiction:																				
– texts which recount experiences and events (autobiography, biography, diary, journal and letter)			●	●							●					●			●	
– journalistic writing																	●			
Text level work:																				
– articulate personal responses to literature						●								●						
– contribute to discussion about literature					●	●								●						
– distinguish between biography and autobiography			●	●												●			●	
– comment on language, style and success of nonfiction texts			●	●								●				●	●			
– understand features of reports																	●			
– develop skills of biographical and autobiographical writing in role			●	●												●			●	
– use styles and conventions of journalism to report on events				●																
Term 2																				
Read a range of fiction and poetry:																				
– stories from variety of genres	●	●		●	●	●	●	●	●			●	●	●				●		
– range of poetic forms; e.g. kennings																				●
Read a range of nonfiction:																				
– formal writing										●										
Text level work:																				
– understand aspects of narrative structure							●						●							
– recognise how poets manipulate words																				●
– analyse how moods, feelings and attitudes are convey in poetry																				●
– read and interpret poems																				●
– identify key features of different types of literary text	●	●		●	●	●	●	●				●	●	●				●		
– analyse the success of texts and writers in evoking a response in the reader							●						●							
– use different genres as models to write	●	●			●	●												●		
– read and understand examples of official language										●										
– construct effective arguments																		●		

CURRICULUM LINKS

England Literacy Year 6 Extension

Objectives	Elf boy meets Superman® (2–5)	Between outer-earth and inner-earth (6–9)	Lucky Jim (10–13)	Amazing Amy! (14–17)	Krishna and the serpent (18–21)	The children of Lir (22–25)	The mystery of the locked door (26–29)	The rescue (30–33)	Goody Two Shoes (34–37)	School timetable (38–41)	Two letters (42–45)	Hex and the captive city of Hur (46–49)	The secret book (50–53)	Don't count your chickens! (54–57)	Irish legends (58–61)	A surfing champion (62–65)	Bare trees baffle local farmer (66–69)	Mirror image (70–73)	Life of a convict (74–77)	My bass guitar and my computer (78–81)
Term 3 — Read a range of nonfiction: — non-chronological reports															●					
Text level work: — retrieve information from texts															●					
— select appropriate style to suit a specific purpose															●					

Northern Ireland — English (Reading) Year 7 Extension

	Elf boy meets Superman® (2–5)	Between outer-earth and inner-earth (6–9)	Lucky Jim (10–13)	Amazing Amy! (14–17)	Krishna and the serpent (18–21)	The children of Lir (22–25)	The mystery of the locked door (26–29)	The rescue (30–33)	Goody Two Shoes (34–37)	School timetable (38–41)	Two letters (42–45)	Hex and the captive city of Hur (46–49)	The secret book (50–53)	Don't count your chickens! (54–57)	Irish legends (58–61)	A surfing champion (62–65)	Bare trees baffle local farmer (66–69)	Mirror image (70–73)	Life of a convict (74–77)	My bass guitar and my computer (78–81)
Range engage with a range of texts, including: — stories	●	●		●	●	●	●	●				●		●				●		
— poems																				●
— plays													●							
— nonfiction material			●	●						●	●				●	●	●		●	
— visual material							●													
Purpose read for information	●	●	●	●	●	●	●	●	●	●	●	●	●	●	●	●	●	●	●	●
acquire skills necessary to locate information within texts	●	●	●	●	●	●	●	●	●	●	●	●	●	●	●	●	●	●	●	●
learn about themselves and others				●	●	●		●		●	●	●	●			●			●	
Reading activities participate in shared reading	●	●	●	●	●	●	●	●	●	●	●	●	●	●	●	●	●	●	●	●
explore and discuss stories	●	●		●	●	●	●	●				●	●	●			●			
discuss and interpret texts	●	●	●	●	●	●	●	●	●	●	●	●	●	●	●	●	●	●	●	●
represent texts in a range of visual forms and diagrams	●	●		●	●	●	●		●				●	●	●		●		●	●
justify responses using inference, deduction and reference to evidence in text	●	●	●	●	●	●	●	●	●	●	●	●	●	●	●	●	●	●	●	●
consider aspects of stories	●	●		●	●	●	●	●				●	●	●				●		
Expected outcomes respond with sensitivity	●	●	●	●	●	●	●			●		●				●	●	●	●	
discuss intentions of writer		●		●		●	●			●		●	●							●
extend range of their reading	●	●	●	●	●	●	●	●	●	●	●	●	●	●	●	●	●	●	●	●
use variety of reading skills for different reading purposes	●	●	●	●	●	●	●	●	●	●	●	●	●	●	●	●	●	●	●	●
place themselves in someone else's position and extend their capacity for sympathy and empathy	●	●	●			●	●					●		●			●		●	
speculate on situations and predict what may happen	●	●	●	●			●	●										●	●	
model their own writing on forms encountered in their reading	●		●	●		●	●	●						●	●	●		●	●	●

CURRICULUM LINKS

Republic of Ireland
English Language
(Reading/Writing)
6th Class

Texts

Category	Objectives	Elf boy meets Superman® (Pages 2–5)	Between outer-earth and inner-earth (Pages 6–9)	Lucky Jim (Pages 10–13)	Amazing Amy! (Pages 14–17)	Krishna and the serpent (Pages 18–21)	The children of Lir (Pages 22–25)	The mystery of the locked door (Pages 26–29)	The rescue (Pages 30–33)	Goody Two Shoes (Pages 34–37)	School timetable (Pages 38–41)	Two letters (Pages 42–45)	Hex and the captive city of Hur (Pages 46–49)	The secret book (Pages 50–53)	Don't count your chickens! (Pages 54–57)	Irish legends (Pages 58–61)	A surfing champion (Pages 62–65)	Bare trees baffle local farmer (Pages 66–69)	Mirror image (Pages 70–73)	Life of a convict (Pages 74–77)	My bass guitar and my computer (Pages 78–81)
Receptiveness to language	engage with increasing range of text	●	●	●	●	●	●	●	●	●	●	●	●	●	●	●	●	●	●	●	●
	observe modelling of a wide variety of writing genres	●	●	●	●	●	●	●	●	●	●	●		●	●		●		●	●	●
	express reactions to reading experiences	●	●	●	●	●	●	●	●	●	●	●	●	●	●	●	●	●	●	●	●
Competence and confidence	read widely from challenging range of reading material	●	●	●	●	●	●	●	●	●	●	●	●	●	●	●	●	●	●	●	●
Developing cognitive abilities	read and respond to a challenging range of poetry																				●
	have access to a wide range of reading material	●	●	●	●	●	●	●	●	●	●	●	●	●	●	●	●	●	●	●	●
	use comprehension skills	●	●	●	●	●	●	●	●	●	●	●	●	●	●	●	●	●	●	●	●
	skim, scan, take notes and summarise	●	●	●	●	●	●	●	●	●	●	●	●	●	●	●	●	●	●	●	●
	retrieve and interpret information presented in a variety of ways	●	●	●	●	●	●	●	●	●	●	●	●	●	●	●	●	●	●	●	●
	support arguments and opinions with evidence from the text	●	●	●	●	●	●	●	●	●	●	●	●	●	●	●	●	●	●	●	●
	read and interpret different kinds of functional text		●	●							●	●					●	●	●	●	
	explore nonfiction texts for various purposes		●	●							●	●					●	●	●		
	distinguish between fact and opinion																●			●	
	find information relevant to his/her purpose in nonfiction texts		●	●							●	●					●	●	●	●	
	write in a variety of genres	●	●	●	●	●	●	●	●	●				●	●		●		●	●	●
	write for a particular purpose and audience		●	●	●															●	
Emotional and imaginative development	respond to fiction and poetry	●	●			●	●	●		●			●	●	●				●		●
	relate personal experience to the ideas and emotions conveyed in the text								●			●	●	●		●			●		
	examine similarities and differences in various types of text												●		●						
	express a personal reaction to ideas, emotions and images encountered in literature		●	●		●	●	●		●	●	●	●	●	●	●	●	●	●	●	●
	express reactions to poems																				●
	write about relationships between poems and personal experience																				●

CURRICULUM LINKS

Scotland English Language (Reading) Primary 7 Extension

Texts

Objectives	Elf boy meets Superman® (Pages 2–5)	Between outer-earth and inner-earth (Pages 6–9)	Lucky Jim (Pages 10–13)	Amazing Amy! (Pages 14–17)	Krishna and the serpent (Pages 18–21)	The children of Lir (Pages 22–25)	The mystery of the locked door (Pages 26–29)	The rescue (Pages 30–33)	Goody Two Shoes (Pages 34–37)	School timetable (Pages 38–41)	Two letters (Pages 42–45)	Hex and the captive city of Hur (Pages 46–49)	The secret book (Pages 50–53)	Don't count your chickens! (Pages 54–57)	Irish legends (Pages 58–61)	A surfing champion (Pages 62–65)	Bare trees baffle local farmer (Pages 66–69)	Mirror image (Pages 70–73)	Life of a convict (Pages 74–77)	My bass guitar and my computer (Pages 78–81)
Level E																				
• Reading for information:																				
– carry out practical tasks										●										
• Reading for enjoyment:																				
– read a variety of texts	●	●	●	●	●	●	●	●	●	●	●	●	●	●	●	●	●	●	●	●
• Reading to reflect on the writer's ideas and craft:																				
– use previous knowledge and skills to predict content	●	●	●	●		●	●									●			●	
– locate main points of text	●	●	●	●	●	●	●	●	●	●	●	●	●	●	●	●	●	●	●	●
– compare text to own ideas, feelings and opinions		●	●			●	●	●		●	●	●	●	●	●	●	●	●	●	●
– evaluate, infer and make judgements	●	●	●	●	●	●	●	●	●	●	●	●	●	●	●	●	●	●	●	●
– think about audience and writer's purpose		●	●	●															●	
• Awareness of genre:																				
– compare similarities and differences between texts												●		●						

CURRICULUM LINKS

Wales English (Reading)
Year 6 Extension

Texts

Objectives		Elf boy meets Superman® (Pages 2–5)	Between outer-earth and inner-earth (Pages 6–9)	Lucky Jim (Pages 10–13)	Amazing Amy! (Pages 14–17)	Krishna and the serpent (Pages 18–21)	The children of Lir (Pages 22–25)	The mystery of the locked door (Pages 26–29)	The rescue (Pages 30–33)	Goody Two Shoes (Pages 34–37)	School timetable (Pages 38–41)	Two letters (Pages 42–45)	Hex and the captive city of Hur (Pages 46–49)	The secret book (Pages 50–53)	Don't count your chickens! (Pages 54–57)	Irish legends (Pages 58–61)	A surfing champion (Pages 62–65)	Bare trees baffle local farmer (Pages 66–69)	Mirror image (Pages 70–73)	Life of a convict (Pages 74–77)	My bass guitar and my computer (Pages 78–81)
Range:	– develop as independent and reflective readers	●	●	●	●	●	●	●	●	●	●	●	●	●	●	●	●	●	●	●	●
	– read for information, using progressively more challenging texts	●	●	●	●	●	●	●	●	●	●	●	●	●	●	●	●	●	●	●	●
	– read playscripts													●							
	– read and use a wide range of nonfiction sources of information			●	●						●	●				●	●			●	
	– read texts with challenging subject matter that extends thinking		●		●		●		●	●		●		●	●		●	●	●	●	
	– read texts with a variety of structural and organisational features			●	●						●	●		●	●	●	●	●	●	●	●
	– read modern poetry																				●
	– read texts from a variety of cultures and traditions					●	●								●						
	– read myths, legends and traditional stories					●	●								●						
Skills:	– respond imaginatively to plot, characters, ideas, vocabulary and language in literature	●	●	●	●	●	●	●	●	●			●	●	●	●				●	●
	– use inference and deduction and refer to relevant passages to support their opinions	●	●	●	●	●	●	●	●	●	●	●	●	●	●	●	●	●	●	●	●
	– use prediction	●	●	●	●			●	●										●		●
	– read for different purposes, including skimming, scanning and detailed reading	●	●	●	●	●	●	●	●	●	●	●	●	●	●	●	●	●	●	●	●
	– pose questions				●									●							
	– distinguish between fact and opinion																●			●	
	– make succinct notes	●		●						●	●		●	●	●	●				●	●
	– represent information in different forms	●	●		●	●	●	●	●	●	●	●	●	●	●	●	●			●	●
Language development:	– recognise the organisational, structural and presentational features of different types of text		●	●	●						●	●	●	●	●	●	●	●	●		●	●

ELF BOY MEETS SUPERMAN®

Teacher information

Genre:

Humour

Question types and comprehension strategies:

- Analyses and extracts information from a humorous narrative to answer literal, deductive and evaluative questions.
- Makes predictions about a narrative and uses these to plan a role-play.

Worksheet information:

Once the pupils have presented their role-plays, they could use the ideas to write narratives that continue the story of Eden and Josh.

Answers:

Page 4

1. (a) Most of them were staring at him in awe and one child moved in close to him.

   (b) Josh grabs at his trousers.

   The children see his underwear and giggle.

   Some of the children start to tug at Josh's trousers.

   One child gives Josh's camera to Eden.

   Eden takes a photograph of Josh with his trousers down.

2. Teacher check

3. (a) Teacher check

   (b) Teacher check

Page 5

Teacher check

Extension:

Read humorous books by authors like Paul Jennings, Roald Dahl and Andy Griffiths.

Note: 'Superman' is a registered trademark of DC Comics, New York, USA.

ELF BOY MEETS SUPERMAN® – 1

Read the humorous narrative.

Yesterday started out as the worst day of my life.

'But Mum, I can't do it. I just can't.'

'Please, Eden. We need you.'

I sighed. If it wasn't bad enough that Mum and Dad had bought a fairy shop, now they expected me to help out. Hadn't they done enough to ruin my life? Try having a stupid name like Eden. It would be bad enough for a girl, but for a boy it's a disaster.

I tried again. 'Mum, 12-year-old boys just don't dress up like elves and tell stories to little kids. What if someone sees me?'

'Eden, I wouldn't ask you if it wasn't important. There's no-one else who can do it. You know that the actor we hired has fallen sick. And you're so good at drama.'

Mum's face was anxious. I knew she and Dad had put a lot of money into buying the shop. But what if someone from school saw me? I glanced at the customers. There were only little kids and their parents.

So the next thing I knew, I was sitting in the corner of the shop in front of a bunch of four-year-olds, dressed in a green felt costume. I had flatly refused to wear the red striped socks, but I was wearing the sparkly shoes. I felt like an idiot so I began the story as soon as I could. I used different voices for the characters and the kids really seemed to like it. Most of them were staring up at me in awe. One kid even moved so close he was half-sitting on my foot. With only a page to go, I was beginning to feel relieved. It was almost over. But a sentence away from the end, I glanced up— and looked straight into the eyes of Josh Baxter, the toughest kid in my school. My mouth dried up and I froze.

'Hi Eden', he sniggered. 'Or should I say "Elf boy"? Nice outfit.'

I leapt to my feet and tried to think of something to say. Meanwhile, Josh was digging in his backpack. Before I could do anything, he'd whipped out a digital camera.

'I think everyone at school would like to see Eden the Elf boy, don't you?'

I wanted to run but I couldn't. I was surrounded by little kids.

Then one of the boys stood up and tugged at Josh's trousers. 'Leave Mr Elf alone, you meanie. He hasn't finished the story.'

Josh just ignored the kid and aimed the camera at me. But the boy kept tugging at Josh's trousers. They were quite loose and they started to slide down. Josh realised what was happening and had to grab at them with his free hand. But it was too late. The children had seen his underwear and they started to giggle. Before I knew what was happening, more of them had jumped up and begun to tug at Josh's trousers. While he tried to swat them away, one of them grabbed the camera and handed it to me. Just as Josh's trousers reached his ankles, I snapped the perfect picture of him in his Superman® underwear. He yelped, pulled up his trousers and charged out of the shop, with all the customers staring and laughing.

Yesterday started out as the worst day of my life. But it ended up pretty well. I actually quite enjoyed my day as an elf. And I've got photographic evidence that Superman® exists.

ELF BOY MEETS SUPERMAN® – 2

Use the text on page 3 to answer the questions.

❶ Literal

(a) What made Eden think that the children liked his storytelling?

_____

_____

_____

_____

(b) Complete the chain of events that led to Josh leaving the shop.

Josh's trousers start to slide down.

_____

_____

_____

_____

Josh runs out of the shop.

❷ Deductive

Why do you think Eden agreed to do the storytelling?

❸ Evaluative

(a) Write what you think Josh might have thought when he saw Eden dressed up as an elf.

_____

_____

_____

(b) Imagine that Eden's parents ask him to do some storytelling again. Eden agrees, but only under certain conditions. List five conditions you think he might set.

Elf boy meets Superman® – 3

1 Think about the characters of Eden and Josh from the humorous text on page 3 to make some predictions.

	Eden	Josh
Predict what this character might do immediately after the story ends.		
Predict what this character might do that night.		
Predict what this character might do before school the next morning.		

2 Find a partner and discuss both sets of predictions. Circle the ones you like the most. Use these to help you plan and present a humorous role-play that takes place when the characters see each other the next day at school. You can change the names and gender of the characters if you need to (e.g. 'Josh' could become 'Jacinta').

Where does the scene take place?

How does the scene start?

How does the scene end?

3 Practise your role-play. When you are ready, present it to a small group or the class.

BETWEEN OUTER-EARTH AND INNER-EARTH

Teacher information

Genre:

Fantasy

Question types and comprehension strategies:

- Analyses and extracts information from a fantasy to answer literal, deductive and evaluative questions.
- Predicts and makes connections to show comprehension of a text.

Worksheet information:

- Question 2 on page 9 is intended to be a creative activity for those pupils who prefer visual representations.

Answers:

Page 8

1. (a) true   (b) false   (c) false   (d) true
   (e) false
2. Teacher check
3. Teacher check

Page 9

Teacher check

Extension:

Other titles in the fantasy genre include:

The chronicles of Mistmantle: Urchin of the Riding Stars by M I McAllister

The chanters of Tremaris by Kate Constable

Guardians of time 3: The key by Marianne Curley

Stravaganza: city of flowers by Mary Hoffman

Through the tiger's eye by Kerrie O'Connor

Read the fantasy.

Another world exists between the polluted atmosphere of the human world and the clean centre of the earth. Driven by years of neglect and abuse, a group of humans fled to the between-Earth to escape an inevitable, painful death. These beings evolved into half-human creatures, Pollumants, who only survived by adapting to their dark and colourless world. Huge slanted eyes allowed them to see in any light which managed to pierce their gloomy world; sharp claws enabled them to forage for food; and their long, greasy hair covered their bodies to help them to retain body heat.

A rudimentary civilisation developed, with each family group dependent on the strongest male to protect, feed and defend his superiority. Areas were set aside for the disposal of waste, the cultivation of 'dark' food, and for living quarters and leisure activities. Male family leaders met together to discuss community problems and concerns.

One such family leader was Murrkh. Murrkh remembered his great-grandfather telling him stories as a little boy about the world above—once green with trees and plants, with clear blue skies providing expanses of air for birds of all descriptions, and sparkling seas teeming with fish.

As Murrkh waited for his time to speak at the community meeting this day, he was anxious and scared, his body shivering and his heart racing as he contemplated the momentous decision he had come to—to venture above the between-Earth into the world above as he had often dreamt of doing.

He announced his request to the head Pollumant, Sludghe, and the assembled family leaders. He waited patiently as loud grumblings and arguments were voiced by one family leader after another. He had expected that his request would be refused, as no Pollumant for many years had ventured outside the between-Earth. Those who had left previously had never returned.

Finally, Sludghe held up his arms for silence and asked Murrkh why he wanted to go.

'I've heard such wondrous tales of the world above that I feel that I must go to see if it still exists. Otherwise how will I ever be content with what I have and where I am, if there may be something better above?'

'Very well, Murrkh', said Sludghe. 'You have my permission to explore the world above, if it is still there. But remember that sometimes the place where you are is where you are meant to be!'

Murrkh packed his supply of under-water and dark food. Finally, dressed in his ragged clothes and cloak, he began his long silent journey into the world above. He walked and walked until his legs and feet would go no further, rested, then walked again. As time merged from one mega-day into another, he could gradually discern some lightening of the shadows and shapes ahead. The ground beneath his feet tilted steeply upward and the pathway narrowed. Soon he had to twist and turn his head and body to manoeuvre through the rocks. Finally, he dragged himself onto level ground onto an open plain darkly shadowed by black skies and craggy, empty mountains.

As he stared in dismay at the scene before him, a half-human creature with sharp claws, huge slanted eyes and a body covered with long, greasy hair came into view ...

BETWEEN OUTER-EARTH AND INNER-EARTH – 2

Answer the questions using the text on page 7.

❶ Literal

Tick true or false for the statements below.

(a) *The Pollumants were able to develop a basic form of community life.*   True False

(b) *Murrkh was an orphan.*   True False

(c) *Sludghe wanted to venture outside the between-Earth.*   True False

(d) *Murrkh had to prepare for his journey.*   True False

(e) *Murrkh did not discover the above world.*   True False

❷ Deductive

Write a sentence or two using words from the text to show:

(a) The Pollumants were not attractive creatures.

_____

_____

_____

_____

_____

(b) Sludghe knew that the world above was not any better than the between-Earth.

_____

_____

_____

_____

_____

_____

(c) The journey to the world above took a long time.

_____

_____

_____

_____

_____

❸ Evaluative

Answer the questions.

(a) Do you think that Murrkh was pleased when he had discovered the world above? Why or why not?

(b) Was the world above better than between-Earth? Why or why not?

(c) Is it possible that the world as we know it today could be changed to that described in the text? Why or why not?

Prim-Ed Publishing   www.prim-ed.com

BETWEEN OUTER-EARTH AND INNER-EARTH – 3

This page should be used in conjunction with the text on page 7.

1 Use the boxes below to write a short paragraph to predict what may have happened before and after the time frame in the text.

Before	**After**

Imagine that the inhabitants of the world above and those of the between-Earth decided to live together and join the two species, using both worlds to live in.

2 Draw a map of the joined worlds, or write descriptions of the way they could be used.

LUCKY JIM

Teacher information

Genre:

Diary

Question types and comprehension strategies:

- Analyses and extracts information from a diary excerpt to answer literal, deductive and evaluative questions.
- Uses sensory imaging to assist with the overall understanding of the diary's writer.
- Predicts and makes connections to continue a written text.

Worksheet information:

When reading the text, pupils may be encouraged to become the writer and feel his experiences rather than just reading about them.

Answers:

Page 12

1. (a) The Northern Counties Annual Medieval Fair
   (b) crutches
   (c) the plaster cast on his foot
   (d) a parachutist in distress blew off course and landed on James.

2–3. Teacher check

Page 13

Teacher check

Extension:

- Suggest pupils research:
  - events held at medieval festivals.
  - the history of the battles which are re-enacted and/or the countries which hold medieval festivals and battle re-enactments.
- Read literature set in medieval times; for example:

  Catherine, called Birdy by Karen Cushman

  The midwife's apprentice by Karen Cushman

  Proud knight, fair lady by Naomi Lewis

  A single shard by Linda Sue Park

  The magician's apprentice by Sidney and Dorothy Rosen

  The Ramsey scallop by Frances Temple

LUCKY JIM – 1

Read the excerpt from a pupil's diary.

Sunday, 27 February

What a day! In less than ten minutes, it will be 'tomorrow' but I'm not ready for sleep yet. If I don't record the events of this remarkable day now, while they're as clear as crystal in my usually befuddled brain, I may believe I dreamt the whole lot and put it down to my overactive imagination. But hey, that wouldn't be possible ... look at the mountain of evidence to prove it all happened ...

Monday, 28 February

8 am

CD kicks in to rouse me from my slumbers. Nothing unusual there, but get this, I'm not here ... in my room, that is. Everything in the room is familiar, you know, clothes, books and all that stuff but the room itself ...? Nope, definitely a parallel universe!

I attempt to lumber out of my pit. Ouch! What the ...? My right foot is encased in plaster of Paris which has been so richly signed with autographs, it looks like a draft version of 'Who's who'.

I spy a pair of crutches by my bedside. After several frustrating attempts to master the art of 'stick-walking', I manage to reach the door. I must remember not to direct anyone to 'walk this way', today! As I reach for the handle, the door flies open and flattens me against the wall.

'James! James! Oh, where has he ... ah, James, there you are! What on earth are you doing on the floor?'

'Mum! Explain please! How did I get like this?'

'Why, don't you remember? The accident? The aircraft? The parachute? The faulty silk? The hospital? And now here you are, commandeering the spare room.'

'What! You mean I jumped out of a plane? I feel dizzy. I need to sit down. Wow! What an amazing experience that must have been! I can't wait 'til I remember how it felt!'

'Er, no James. You didn't jump. You just happened to be in the wrong place at the wrong time and you were, how shall I say, 'landed upon'.

'Now then, what would you like for breakfast?'

11 am

Well, I've had time to recall yesterday's spectacular aerial incident and here I am, 'back in time' at the Northern Counties Annual Medieval Fair. Let's hope there are no low-flying, off-course parachutists in the vicinity! I'm getting used to hobbling around in style, with Bill and Ben, my crutches. I thought I should name them, after all, we're going to be spending rather a lot of time together! I'm here at the magnificent falconry display now. That should be harmless enou ...

Aagh, that was close! I thought they could keep these birds under control! Something trickling down my face ... blood!

2.30 pm

They're getting to know me quite well here. It's like a home from home. Even the bed here has my name on it! I fancy being a doctor when I grow up. I think I'd look really cool, swanning around in a lab. coat, sporting a trendy stethoscope.

Half a dozen stitches this time which I must say is not too bad considering I could have lost an eye. Lucky Jim. That's what everyone's calling me.

Right, just enough time to get back to the fair to watch the jousting ...

LUCKY JIM – 2

Refer to the text on page 11 to answer the questions.

❶ Literal

(a) What event was James attending when he sustained his second injury?

(b) Circle the correct answer.

Bill and Ben were James's

friends   **brothers**

crutches   **neighbours**

(c) What was the 'mountain of evidence' James refers to in paragraph one?

_____

_____

_____

(d) What happened to cause James's original injury?

_____

_____

_____

❷ Deductive

(a) Write three adjectives you think best describe James's personality.

(b) Using examples from the text, explain how you reached this decision.

_____

_____

(c) Where was James at 2.30 pm? How do you know?

_____

_____

❸ Evaluative

(a) Why do you think James is now sleeping in the spare room? _____

_____

_____

(b) What might your life be like if you had James's injuries?

Advantages	**Disadvantages**

LUCKY JIM – 3

With reference to the text on page 11, complete these questions.

1 (a) Write a brief explanation of the medieval sport of jousting.

_____

_____

_____

_____

_____

(b) What do you think are the chances of James returning home without further incident? Tick a box.

| Likely | Unlikely |

Why?_____

_____

(c) In the box, write suggestions for what calamities might befall James at the jousting contest. Include any journeys he might make and the transport used.

2 Using your suggestions, write the entry for James's diary until 6 pm. Make your entry read as though James has written it.

AMAZING AMY!

Teacher information

Genre:

Journal

Question types and comprehension strategies:

- Analyses and extracts information from a journal to answer literal, deductive and evaluative questions.
- Makes connections between text and character traits.
- Makes predictions about a journal text.

Worksheet information:

Amy Johnson joined the Air Transport Auxiliary in 1939—the start of World War II. She was a member of a group of experienced pilots whose flying duties included ferrying aircraft from factory airstrips to RAF bases. On 5 January 1941, during one of these routine flights, Amy crashed into the Thames estuary and was drowned. Her body was never recovered.

Answers:

Page 16

1. (a) Amy sought an investor because, despite her qualifications, she was unable to earn a living as a pilot.

   (b) Bert Hinkler was an Australian pilot who flew from England to Australia in 15 days.

   (c) Amy was frightened on the fourth day of her adventure by the sound of what she thought were 'desert dogs'.

   (d) Amy crash-landed into a football field in Rangoon, India, on the ninth day of her journey. She had to wait three days for repairs, delaying her and making it impossible for her to beat Hinkler's record of 15 days.

   (e) Amy departed England with only a handful of spectators but returned to a parade of possibly a million people lining the streets.

2–3. Teacher check

Page 17

Teacher check

Extension:

Read other historical novels like:

Playing Beatie Bow by Ruth Park

Diary of a young girl by Anne Frank

Arthur: The seeing stone by Kevin Crossley-Holland

Amazing Amy! – 1

Read the fictional extracts from the journal of heroic aviator – Amy Johnson.

17 July 1929
Today is a day for celebration! I have earnt my pilot's licence!
Let those who tried to dampen my spirit with their doubts and
archaic beliefs know that I will fly the sky as their equal, if not their superior!

3 December 1929
I have come to the conclusion that I must seek out an investor, for I am rich in qualifications—a
pilot, a navigator, a ground engineer—yet I can barely afford to feed myself! If I wish to earn a
living as a pilot, then I must have my own plane!

4 May 1930
The day before my grandest adventure! I leave England in the morn—bound for Australia. My
saviour, Lord Wakefield (rich in oil and a believer in dreams), has given me the capital to purchase
a plane. It's a beautiful green Moth that I've named 'Jason', after the family business. I shall fly to
Australia in less than 15 days and beat the record of the Australian, Bert Hinkler.

8 May 1930
My fourth day of flying. I landed in the desert to the frightful sound of desert dogs. With my gun
at hand, I waited for them to appear so they might rip me to shreds. Thankfully, no such creature
revealed itself to me.

11 May 1930
Reached Karachi in splendid time! I've travelled 4000 miles and improved on Hinkler's record by two
wonderful days! It amuses me that I left England to only a handful of well-wishers and no journalist to
report on my venture (perhaps as they thought it too absurd to be real) and now I may not only be the
first woman to fly solo to Australia but the first pilot to do so in under 15 days!

14 May 1930
Nine days in the air, battling monsoon rains and blistering heat, and I've crash-landed my beautiful
Moth into a football field in Rangoon, India. They say it will be three days before she is in the air again.
Impossible!

24 May 1930
I've journeyed 11 000 miles—an admirable feat but I feel a failure. The Australians, in Darwin where I
landed, have been jolly good sports, calling me an heroic adventurer. Alas, I don't feel heroic. I feel weary
and second best.
'The Daily Mail' (who thought my departure was not newsworthy) are awarding me ten thousand pounds
for such a daring feat! They say a telegram from the King and Queen should also be expected!

July 1930
It has been one year since I earnt my pilot's licence. Today I was driven through the streets of London
in a parade so that one million English fans could welcome me home!

July 1932
London to Cape Town in 11 hours! I have finally broken a record! Now I must plan my next adventure.
I think England to New York!

January 1941
The whole world has changed! We continue to ferry pilots and aircraft from the
factories to the RAF bases. At least I am contributing to the war effort. The
weather has been disastrous of late! Thick fog and freezing. I head off again
tomorrow.

AMAZING AMY! – 2

Use the text on page 15 to answer the questions.

➊ Literal

(a) What factors prompted Amy to seek out an investor to finance a plane?

_____

(b) Who is Bert Hinkler?

_____
_____
_____

(c) What frightens Amy on 8 May 1930?

_____
_____
_____

(d) What event delays Amy's attempt at the record?

_____

(e) How does Amy's departure from England compare to her return?

_____
_____

➋ Deductive

Answer these questions by giving evidence from the text.

(a) Why does Amy refer to Lord Wakefield as a 'believer in dreams'?

```
┌─────────────────────────────────────┐
│                                      │
│                                      │
│                                      │
│                                      │
└─────────────────────────────────────┘
```

(b) Why does Amy feel second-best when she arrives in Darwin?

_____
_____
_____
_____

(c) What do you think Amy means by the remark that the 'whole world has changed' in her final entry?

_____
_____
_____

➌ Evaluative

(a) Who do you think it was that 'tried to dampen Amy's spirit with their doubts and archaic beliefs'?

_____
_____
_____
_____

(b) Amy Johnson is known as Britain's most famous pilot. Why do you think she earnt so much fame?

```
┌─────────────────────────────────────┐
│                                      │
│                                      │
│                                      │
│                                      │
│                                      │
│                                      │
│                                      │
│                                      │
└─────────────────────────────────────┘
```

Amazing Amy! – 3

Use the text on page 15 to complete the activities.

1 (a) When you read the text about aviator Amy Johnson, what questions come to mind about her and her life? Discuss your thoughts with a partner and record your questions in the boxes below.

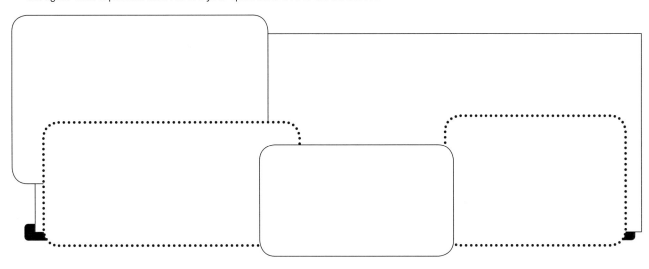

(b) Join with another pair of pupils and discuss possible answers to your questions. Circle one of the questions above and write below the answer that your group agreed upon.

_____

_____

_____

2 Imagine that the journal entry dated January 1941 was Amy Johnson's last entry. What happened to her?

Create the *Daily Mail*'s front page article that explains why it was Amy's final entry in her journal. Include some information about Amy's achievements and the type of person she was. Invent a headline that is short but will grab the reader's attention. Include a drawing you think matches the story.

Daily Mail	**6 January 1941**

KRISHNA AND THE SERPENT

Teacher information

Genre:

Myth

Question types and comprehension strategies:

- Analyses and extracts information from a myth to answer literal, deductive and evaluative questions.
- Makes connections between text and character traits.
- Compares similarities and differences between his or her own character rating and that of other class members.

Worksheet information:

- Discuss how myths give a religious explanation for something and how, unlike legends, no opinion is expressed as to whether they are true or not.
- Pupils should complete both activity pages independently, as working closely with another class member may influence their character rating on page 21, and comparing answers will not be as effective.

Answers:

Page 20

1. (a) dark, handsome child; beautiful clothes; attractive ornaments; long dark hair; tightly coiled hair

   (b) fish, wading birds, crocodiles, forest trees, people

2. (a) (i) contaminated (5)   (ii)   treacherous (6)

      (iii) purposefully (6)   (iv)   merciful (8)

      (v) exhilarated (9)   (vi)   pleaded (8)

      (vii) banished (8)   (viii) wistful (4)

      (ix) lilting (3)   (x)   revered (1)

   (b) Teacher check

3. Teacher check

Page 21

Teacher check

Extension:

- Prim-Ed Publishing produces a comprehension series based on myths and fables, with accompanying reading, comprehension and writing activities. A title suitable for this age group is: *Read, understand and write* – Myths Book 2 (code 0238).
- Pupils who would enjoy reading other Indian myths could go to the website <http://www. 4to40.com> and follow the prompts from 'Katha' (Indian myths).

KRISHNA AND THE SERPENT – 1

Read the myth.

Lord Krishna is one of the most revered deities (gods) in the Hindu faith and there are numerous myths involving him, many of which depict him destroying evil powers. The story of Krishna and the serpent, Kaliyan, is very well known. It is set near the Yamuna River, which, along with the Ganges, is one of the most sacred rivers in India.

Krishna lived in a village near the Yamuna River. He was a dark, handsome child who always wore beautiful clothes adorned with attractive ornaments. Krishna's long dark hair was coiled tightly around on top of his head and tied in a knot, into which he often placed a peacock's feather.

Krishna was a charming child and liked by everyone—even when he was yet again found playing pranks on people. He delighted in listening to and playing music and was an excellent flautist. Whenever he played on his flute, everyone would stop what they were doing to come and listen to his lilting tunes. Even the wild jungle animals would quieten at the sound of his flute.

Krishna's job was to help take the cattle into the jungle near the river every morning and bring them home in the evening. Here there was plenty of grass for them to graze on and water to drink. One day, as Krishna was playing a wistful tune to the other cowherds, a huge, poisonous serpent named Kaliyan slithered past them and slunk into the river. He had decided to make his new home in the deepest part.

Soon, however, the river became contaminated by Kaliyan's poison. Any person or animal that drank from the river fell dead. Poisoned fish, wading birds and crocodiles floated upside down in the water. Even the forest trees on the river bank shrivelled up and died. The river was the source of fresh water for all living things surrounding the area and great suffering was endured by all.

Krishna decided to teach the treacherous serpent a lesson. He walked purposefully up to the river bank, jumped in at the deepest part and swam to Kaliyan's home. Kaliyan immediately launched himself at Krishna to crush him to death. But Krishna was too quick and swam to the surface, followed by Kaliyan. In an instant, Krishna got hold of Kaliyan's head and stood on it. Kaliyan tried in vain to shake him off. He dived deep into the water with Krishna still secured firmly on his head. Kaliyan's plan was to try to drown Krishna, but Krishna was able to hold his breath for as long as he wanted. Kaliyan was forced to swim back to the surface for air.

Throngs of terrified villagers gathered on the river bank to witness Krishna's struggle with the hated serpent. Kaliyan tried to twist around to bite Krishna, who managed to get both his hands around the serpent's head. He began kicking the snake as hard as he could. Slowly but surely, Kaliyan began to weaken, as he could not withstand the pain of Krishna's assault. He started spurting poison, but Krishna continued to attack him until all the poison had come out.

Finally, the huge serpent gave up the struggle and pleaded with Krishna to spare his life. Krishna heard his plea and decided to be merciful. He banished Kaliyan from the Yamuna. Kaliyan slithered painfully away, never to be seen again.

The exhilarated villagers cheered Krishna as he swam ashore. Thanks to his almighty feat, the river was pure once more.

KRISHNA AND THE SERPENT – 2

Use the text on page 19 to answer the questions.

❶ Literal

(a) From the second paragraph list four separate phrases which describe Krishna's appearance.

_____

_____

_____

_____

(b) List four living things that perished after being poisoned by Kaliyan's actions.

_____

_____

_____

_____

❷ Deductive

(a) Write a synonym from the text for each word below and in the box write the number of the paragraph it is found in.

(i) **polluted** _____

(ii) **dangerous** _____

(iii) **determinedly** _____

(iv) **forgiving** _____

(v) **delighted** _____

(vi) **begged** _____

(vii) **banned** _____

(viii) **thoughtful** _____

(ix) **rhythmical** _____

(x) **honoured** _____

(b) There is evidence in the story to suggest Krishna possessed special powers. Give two examples of this.

❸ Evaluative

(a) Do you think Kaliyan deserved Krishna's mercy? Explain your answer in detail.

....

....

....

(b) How else could Krishna have taught the serpent a lesson ?

....

....

....

KRISHNA AND THE SERPENT – 3

Use the text on page 19 to complete the activity.

Complete the character ratings for Krishna and Kaliyan, then compare your answers with those of other class members.

Krishna's character rating

	Extremely	A bit	Can't tell	A bit	Extremely	
Kind						**Cruel**
Comment						
Fearless						**Cowardly**
Comment						
Friendly						**Unfriendly**
Comment						
Strong-willed						**Weak-willed**
Comment						
Generous						**Selfish**
Comment						

Kaliyan's character rating

	Extremely	A bit	Can't tell	A bit	Extremely	
Kind						**Cruel**
Comment						
Fearless						**Cowardly**
Comment						
Friendly						**Unfriendly**
Comment						
Strong-willed						**Weak-willed**
Comment						
Generous						**Selfish**
Comment						

THE CHILDREN OF LIR

Teacher information

Genre:

Folktale

Question types and comprehension strategies:

- Analyses and extracts information from a folktale to answer literal, deductive and evaluative questions.
- Determines the importance of particular events within the text.
- Makes connections between characters to create a family tree.

Worksheet information:

- When reading the text, pupils may be encouraged to consider the story from each character's position.
- Completing the family tree on page 25 will clarify the relationships among the characters as information presented in graphical form is more visual and obvious.

Answers:

Page 24

1. (a) the Lake of the Red Eye, the Sea of Moyle, the land of Erris

    (b) Lairgnen, the man from the north and Doech, the woman from the south

    (c) the children kept their voices and could sing beautifully

2–3. Teacher check

Page 25

1. Teacher check

2. (a)

```
                              King Dearg
              Lir (m) Ove                    Oifa (m) Lir
         Aod    Fingula  Fiachra  Conn
```

    (b) Grandfather (grandparent)

    (c) Stepmother and aunt

Extension:

Suggest that pupils:

- research other Celtic folktales from Ireland, Wales, Scotland, Cornwall in England and Brittany in France.
- locate real places mentioned in tales on a map of the abovementioned Celtic regions.
- research Celtic place names; e.g. Erin and Albain are the Celtic names for Ireland and Scotland.

The children of Lir – 1

Read this Irish folktale.

The five kings of Erin met to decide who would become overall king of the isle. King Lir of the Hill of the White Field expected to be elected. When King Dearg was chosen, Lir was incensed and he returned home feeling great outrage. The other three wanted to kill Lir for his refusal to acknowledge Dearg as chieftain. Dearg restrained them, requesting that their lives remain peaceful.

To pacify Lir, Dearg offered him the hand of his eldest daughter, Ove. Lir and Ove were very happy and were soon blessed with twins, a son, Aod, and a daughter, Fingula. A while later, the twin sons Fiachra and Conn were born. Sadly, Ove did not live long enough to hold them in her arms or even to lay her motherly eyes upon them.

Lir mourned bitterly for his beloved wife and, had it not been for his children whom he loved dearly, he would have died of grief. In time, Lir married Ove's sister, Oifa, who was full of love and affection for Lir and his four children. But as Lir's love for his children grew deeper than his love for her, Oifa grew jealous and bitter. Soon her feelings for the children of Lir were those of hatred and simmering rage.

One day, Oifa took the children to the Lake of the Red Eye. As they were bathing in the cool, clear waters, she cast a spell and turned them into four beautiful, white swans.

'Like this you will stay for 900 years, until Lairgnen, the man from the north, marries Deoch, the woman from the south. But I will grant you two things, you will retain your voices and your songs will be the sweetest-sounding arias ever heard.'

Lir knew that Oifa had somehow harmed his children. He set off towards the lake where he was confronted with the reality of Oifa's cruel work. He was distraught. As he bade his children farewell, he knew his life would never again know happiness.

When King Dearg heard of Oifa's malicious deed, he used his Druid wand for spells and sorcery against her, compelling her to spend eternity in a life of misery as an air demon.

The people were so sadly grieved at the loss of the children that it was decreed that no swan would ever again be killed on the isle of Erin.

For 300 years, the children of Lir spent their time on the Lake of the Red Eye, captivating everyone with their enchanting songs. Eventually, the time came for the swans to fly to the open Sea of Moyle between Erin and Albain. Here they would spend 300 years in cold and misery, ravaged by hunger and violent storms. The swans endured another 300 miserable years in the desolate land of Erris, before returning home to the Hill of the White Field. But how everything had changed! Ruins and overgrown gardens were all that was left of their once charming home; just bleak desolation and decay.

At this time, Lairgnen, prince of the north, was to marry Deoch, daughter of the king of the south. She had heard of the magnificent swans with their beautiful singing voices. She refused to marry Lairgnen until he captured them for her as a wedding present. Lairgnen was close to achieving this goal but, as he touched the wings of the birds, they lost their feathers and transformed back to their human forms. But time had not stood still for them, no longer were they young children full of life and joy, but four wizened and withered old folk, ready for the grave.

The four were buried together and a cairn was raised for them. Such was the fate of the children of Lir.

To this day, no-one is allowed to kill a swan in Ireland, the land of Erin.

THE CHILDREN OF LIR – 2

Answer these questions relating to the text on page 23.

❶ Literal

(a) Where did the swans spend each 300-year period?

_____

_____

_____

(b) Before the swans could be released, who had to be married?

_____

_____

_____

(c) What parting gifts did Oifa leave with the children of Lir?

_____

_____

_____

❸ Evaluative

(a) Why do you think it was decreed that no swans should be killed on the isle of Erin?

❷ Deductive

(a) How do you think the children felt when they returned home to the Hill of the White Field? Explain your answer.

(b) Tick the correct box.

(i) Lir was happy that Dearg was chosen as chieftain. **True** **False**

(ii) Lir was a doting father. **True** **False**

(iii) The children enjoyed their time as swans. **True** **False**

(iv) Dearg was a righteous king. **True** **False**

(b) Choose a character from this sad folktale.

King Lir ☐   **King Dearg** ☐   **Oifa** ☐   **the children of Lir** ☐

(c) Explain why your chosen character felt sad.

....

....

....

....

....

THE CHILDREN OF LIR – 3

1 The story naturally falls into four parts. Consider where you think the divisions occur and place these events in the correct boxes in chronological order.

- Lir and Oifa marry
- swans in the Sea of Moyle
- swans revert to human form
- Oifa turned to air demon
- swans return home

- children turned into swans
- decree that no swans be killed
- King Dearg elected as chieftain
- swans in the land of Erris
- swans at the Lake of Red Eye

- Ove dies
- children die
- Lir and Ove wed
- children born

Part one
_____
_____
_____
_____
_____

Part two
_____
_____
_____
_____
_____

Part three
_____
_____
_____
_____

Part four
_____
_____
_____
_____

2 (a) Complete the family tree for the children of Lir.

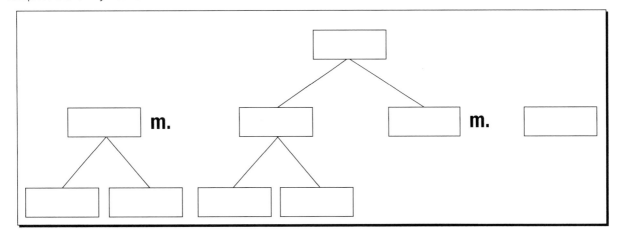

(b) What relation is King Dearg to the children of Lir?

(c) What two categories of relationship does Oifa have with the children?

THE MYSTERY OF THE LOCKED DOOR

Teacher information

Genre:

Mystery

Question types and comprehension strategies:

- Analyses and extracts information from a mystery to answer literal, deductive and evaluative questions.
- Makes connections between a text and the conventions of the mystery genre to plot a chapter.

Worksheet information:

- Before pupils complete the activity on page 29, teachers could hold a class discussion on mystery novels or stories the pupils have read and ask them to describe their plots.
- After the pupils complete the activity, they can try writing their chapters on a separate sheet of paper.

Answers:

Page 28

1. (a) (i) false (ii) true
      (iii) false (iv) true
   (b) She wants to see if there is anything behind the tapestry.
   (c) Teacher check
2. She is worried he might have seen her watching him.
3. Teacher check

Page 29

Teacher check

Extension:

Read other mystery titles like:

Antonio S and the mystery of Theodore Guzman by Odo Hirsch

Emily Eyefinger series by Duncan Ball

Encyclopedia Brown series by Donald J Sobol

The Roman mysteries series by Caroline Lawrence

THE MYSTERY OF THE LOCKED DOOR – 1

Read the chapter from a mystery novel.

CHAPTER 6

Kate held her breath as she watched her uncle carefully place the key inside the photo frame. So that's where he kept it. She couldn't believe it had taken her two weeks of her holiday with her aunt and uncle to find out. Kate ducked back around the corner and hoped he hadn't seen her.

'Kate?'

Her heart pounding, she walked into the room. 'Yes, Uncle Stanley?'

'I'm going out for a walk. You stay here and don't get into any trouble. Your aunt will be back any minute now.'

'Okay.' She tried not to look too excited.

He glared at her for a few seconds, tapped his cane and stalked towards the front door.

As soon as Kate heard the door slam, she headed for the fireplace and retrieved the key from inside the photo frame. Finally, she was going to find out why Uncle Stanley always locked the door to the attic. She turned and raced up the stairs, reaching the door within seconds. Her hands shook as she fitted the key into the lock. Kate paused for a moment, then pushed open the door. It was dark inside and she felt for the light switch. She flicked it on and took in the scene in front of her.

The room was filled with all kinds of junk—stacks of boxes, neglected wooden furniture and piles of clothing. It smelt musty, making Kate feel queasy. Trying to ignore it, she looked around. Why had her uncle gone to so much trouble to keep her out of here? What was his secret? Kate's eyes fell on a small table near the far wall. She could see a handprint in the thick layer of dust on the table. She walked over and examined it. Someone must have been here recently.

Her eyes flicked up to the wall behind the table. The mournful eyes of a woman gazed at her from a mouldy-looking tapestry.

Kate shivered. 'What's going on?' she whispered.

She knew it was silly to talk to a tapestry, but she felt as though this woman was hiding a secret. Was she? A thought struck her. Could there be something behind the tapestry?

Kate carefully squeezed into the gap between the table and the wall. Then she reached out and moved the tapestry to one side. She gasped.

THE MYSTERY OF THE LOCKED DOOR – 2

Answer these questions about the text on page 27.

❶ Literal

Answer the questions.

(a) True or false?

    (i) Kate felt queasy because she was frightened.

    True **False**

    (ii) Uncle Stanley had hidden the key to the attic.

    True **False**

    (iii) Kate knew someone had been near the table because it had been cleaned.

    True **False**

    (iv) Kate was in a hurry to get to the attic.

    True **False**

(b) Why does Kate squeeze into the gap between the wall and the table? _____

_____

(c) List words or phrases that describe Uncle Stanley. _____

_____

❷ Deductive

(a) Why do you think Kate's heart was pounding when she went to talk to Uncle Stanley?

_____

_____

❸ Evaluative

(a) Imagine Uncle Stanley sneaks back into the house and catches Kate as she is running up the stairs. Write what you think they would say to each other.

Uncle Stanley:	**Kate:**	**Uncle Stanley:**	**Kate:**

(b) The chapter is written from Kate's point of view. Write it instead from the point of view of the mournful-eyed woman in the tapestry. Below, begin with her hearing Kate run up the stairs. Finish on a separate sheet of paper.

....

....

....

THE MYSTERY OF THE LOCKED DOOR – 3

Mystery novels are full of mysterious or puzzling elements.

1 List some examples of mysterious or puzzling elements a mystery novel might use.

> secret codes, the disappearance of someone, a locked room,

2 Use your ideas to help you plan the next chapter of *The mystery of the locked door*. To begin, write two possibilities for what Kate might find behind the tapestry. Circle the one you like better, then continue the process down the page. Part of Chapter 6 has been done as an example.

Kate sees Uncle Stanley hide the key

What happens next?	Kate follows Uncle Stanley	OR	Kate steals the key
What happens next?	Kate finds	OR	Kate finds
What happens next?		OR	
What happens next?		OR	
What happens next?		OR	
What happens next?		OR	

How do you want your chapter to end? To keep a reader turning pages, mystery novel chapters often end on a note of suspense.

3 List some suspenseful ways a mystery novel chapter might end.

> someone reveals his/her true personality, a menacing shadow appears behind the main character,

4 Describe two possibilities for a suspenseful ending for your chapter. Tick the one you like better.

THE RESCUE

Teacher information

Genre:

Adventure

Question types and comprehension strategies:

- Analyses and extracts information from an adventure story to answer literal, deductive and evaluative questions.
- Uses sensory imaging to set the scene for the reader.
- Predicts and makes connections between the text and its characters traits.

Worksheet information:

- Clarify any terms pupils are unsure of from the text on page 31; for example:

  Ute – Australian for 'utility', which is a car with a cargo area at the back; a pick-up.

  Yabby – Australian freshwater crayfish.

  Dam – a pond for farm use, with built up walls on the sides, constructed by an excavator.

  Dinky – Carrying a passenger on the front or back of a bicycle or motorbike.

- Pupils may reread the text and highlight phrases or sentences that describe the scene using the five senses—sight, sound, smell, taste and touch.

- Pupils may write a paragraph describing any personal connections they made to the text. These connections may have occurred due to prior knowledge of the setting or new information presented in the text. Pupils may comment on the author's use of the senses to describe the scene or discuss a similar adventure they had with a group of friends. Pupils may also have connected to the text due to experiences on a farm or fishing in a dam.

- If pupils are having difficulty continuing the story, as directed on page 33, Question 2, ask them prompting questions such as:

  – Was Mr Bell happy the boys saved the sheep?

  – How did he react to the boys taking his ute without permission?

  – How did he react to Shane driving his ute (without a licence)?

  – Was Mrs Bell happy to have the three buckets of yabbies for tea?

  – Do the boys have to cook and peel the yabbies themselves?

  – Are the boys punished for taking the ute?

Answers:

Page 32

1. (a) (i) False (ii) True (iii) True (iv) False
2. Teacher check
3. Teacher check

Page 33

Teacher check

Extension:

Other adventure stories include:

Alanna: The first adventure by Tamora Pierce

The dark is rising by Susan Cooper   *The railway children* by E Nesbitt

THE RESCUE – 1

Read the adventure story.

Colin knows he's showing off but he doesn't care. He rides around the petrol pumps, does a 'doughnut' on the grass and skids dangerously close to a heap of rusting scrap metal that is the graveyard for the farm's old vehicles. He skids to a halt by the two boys who are leaning against their own Honda 50 cc motorbikes, covering them with red dust. Colin removes his helmet and grins at his two best mates.

''Bout time you guys got here! Let's go in. Mum's making us some lunch to take with us.' The boys follow the waft of bacon over to the house and collect their lunch from Mrs Bell. They drain some rainwater from the tank into their drink bottles and grab a yabby net each from the shed. As they walk back to the bikes, Simon notices that Colin's Honda is on a slant.

'Heh, Col! Think you might have a flat!'

Colin curses under his breath.

'Stupid junk metal! There's a giant gash in my tyre!' he declares angrily.

'I could dinky you on my bike but with our backpacks and the nets, it'll be a slow trip', suggests Shane.

Simon has an idea. After some persuasion, Colin agrees to take Mr Bell's old ute from the shed, but only if Shane drives. As his dad lets him drive around the farm on weekends, Shane excitedly agrees. The boys throw the yabby nets in the back of the ute and drive away from the house. The sound of the ute leaving alerts the sheepdogs, who bark their farewell.

The first dam the boys arrive at is nearly empty. Dead yabbies are floating on top of the mud and the ducks are enjoying a mid-morning feast.

'Phew! This dam stinks!' Shane remarks, putting the ute into reverse. The boys drive along the fence road to the next dam, which is completely dry.

'It'd better rain soon', says Simon, almost in a whisper. The other boys nod in silence, contemplating the consequences of another bad season.

Pulling up at the lip of the third dam, the ute scares a flock of sheep from their drinking hole. The boys cheer as they see it's full of fresh water. The nets are collected and slimy chunks of raw meat are skewered onto the metal hooks. Each boy drops a net into the murky, brown water of the dam. They sit on its banks and begin digging around in their backpacks for their sandwiches.

With his mouth full of homemade bread, warm bacon and runny egg, Simon realises he can hear a strange noise. 'Woz dat 'oise?' he asks, his words muffled. A panicked cry echoes across the paddock.

Colin jumps up and walks over the other side of the dam. 'Look at this! I think she's in trouble! Shane, grab that old shirt from under the seat in the ute.' One of Colin's dad's prized ewes is on its side, the back legs of a tiny lamb jutting out from behind it.

'It's definitely stuck!' Colin takes the shirt from Shane and places it around the tiny back legs of the lamb. With a gentle pull, the lamb is out, spluttering and bleating. Colin takes the lamb around for its mother to smell and get its scent. The ewe isn't interested.

'Can you two lift her onto the back of the ute?' asks Colin, carrying the lamb towards the dam. 'We can put them in a small pen in the sheep yards at home. She'll have to let the lamb near her then.'

With the ewe and its lamb securely on the back of the ute, the boys walk over to where they dropped the nets.

'OK. Let's pull them in!' The boys carefully drag the nets onto the dam's bank and find them overflowing with yabbies. They tip them out onto the bank, chasing the escapees who shuffle backwards to the water. The boys sort the yabbies—big ones in the buckets, smaller ones go back in the dam.

With their buckets full to the brim, they carry them to the ute.

'Heh, Colin. I think your dad's gonna realise we took his ute when we show up with the ewe and the lamb', remarks Simon, watching the lamb trying unsuccessfully to get a drink from its mother. 'At least we saved the lamb, right?'

'... And we've got three buckets of yabbies for tea!' offers Shane.

Colin climbs into the front of the ute, thinking.

'Well … we're about to find out!'

THE RESCUE – 2

Answer these questions about the text from page 31.

❶ Literal

(a) True or false?

   (i) Shane is chosen to drive the ute as he is the biggest and can reach the pedals.

      ☐ True   ☐ False

   (ii) The second dam the boys go to is completely dry.

      ☐ True   ☐ False

   (iii) Raw meat is used to bait the nets to catch the yabbies.

      ☐ True   ☐ False

   (iv) The larger yabbies are thrown back into the dam.

      ☐ True   ☐ False

❸ Evaluative

(a) How old do you think the boys are? _____

(b) What type of character do you think Colin is?

❷ Deductive

(a) Why don't the boys take the two motorbikes to the dam?

(b) Why are the boys taking the ewe and the lamb back to the farm?

(c) Why were the larger yabbies taken and the smaller ones put back in the dam?

_____

_____

_____

(c) *'It'd better rain soon', says Simon, almost in a whisper. The other boys nod in silence, contemplating the consequences of another bad season.*

What do these two sentences tell us about life on a farm? Make some notes below.

THE RESCUE – 3

Answer these questions about the text from page 31.

To help readers imagine a clear picture of a setting in a story, authors often use the five senses to describe the scene. This can help readers to enjoy the story, especially if the setting is a place that is foreign to them, such as an Australian farm.

1 (a) Reread the story. Highlight the sentences or phrases that describe the scene using one of the senses. Record your findings in the boxes below in point form.

What did the boys see?	What did the boys hear?	What did they smell?

What did they touch?	What did they taste?

(b) Did you have a clear picture of the boys on the farm when you read the story? In your answer, include what helped you to make connections to the text (for example, the senses described, having visited a farm before or having read other stories similar to this one).

_____

_____

_____

_____

2 What happens when the boys arrive back at the house? Finish the story by writing the final paragraph. Include dialogue between the boys and Mr Bell. (Continue on the back of this sheet.)

....

....

....

....

....

....

....

....

....

....

GOODY TWO SHOES

Teacher information

Genre:

Horror

Question types and comprehension strategies:

- Analyses and extracts information from a horror/supernatural narrative to answer literal, deductive and evaluative questions.
- Makes comparisons and connections from the text to create character profiles.
- Determines important information to analyse key elements of a story.

Worksheet information:

On page 37, pupils should be encouraged to compare the different points of view on each of the criteria. Mr Wizard may focus on his neatness and good grooming, while Ben might be more likely to describe the more disturbing aspects of his appearance; for example, his eyes.

Answers:

Page 36

1. (a) (iii) he wanted to help his father.
2. (a) (ii) something strange had happened to his friends.
    (b) Jake looked and acted differently.
3. Teacher check

Page 37

Teacher check

Extension:

- Pupils compile lists of authors and titles of the horror/supernatural genre.
- Brainstorm the different characteristics and features of this genre.
- Discuss the effectiveness of leaving 'what happens next' to the readers imagination.

GOODY TWO SHOES – 1

Read the horror narrative.

You should see this new teacher at our school. He's old with thick grey hair and he wears an immaculate suit and tie. His trousers have a crease down the front that is so sharp it could cut butter and his shoes shine so brightly we need sunglasses for the glare. We decided it would be fun to try the old guy out; he looked a pretty easy target. But despite our best efforts, he stayed calm, cool, and collected. He ignored most of what we did until my friend, Jake, spilt some stuff all over the kid who sits in front of him. Mr Wizard stared at him with his strange, almost colourless eyes and suggested that they should have a meeting after school. A detention on day one, that must be a record even for Jake!

I phoned Jake tonight to see how he got on. Jake sounded a bit subdued and different. He just said that the old guy had talked to him for a while, offered him a drink and some biscuits and sent him home. Going down to the river to mess around as we often do seemed a good idea, but when I suggested it, Jake said something about wanting to help his dad with the garden. That's a joke, he must have something really special planned, can't wait to hear about it tomorrow. I phoned Alex and we wandered down to the river where we smashed a few bottles, threw some rocks into the water and onto some roofs until a mean, ugly looking dog started to make a racket and we decided we'd better get out of there.

I just can't understand it. Jake arrived at school this morning with his shirt tucked in, his hair combed and he actually worked hard. He spoke politely, offered to do boring jobs and he'd even done his homework! He must be sick. Alex had scrawled 'homework stinks' all over his paper because, like me, he didn't even have time to look at it. I escaped but he got a detention. I don't think Mr Wizard has a home, he seems to be here all the time. He's not like any teacher I've ever had before.

Alex got a ridiculously high mark for his homework today and he really looked like he cared. He seems different. I'm not sure what it is but the funloving, into anything friend I have been in so much trouble with has disappeared. It's scary. He and Jake were talking about joining the scouts so they could do some community service. They're weird! I feel as if they're strangers. I can't understand them.

I've got a detention after school! All I did was add some purple stuff to the class fish tank. The fish are a bit lethargic but still alive. I thought it looked cool, but Mr Wizard didn't agree. Boy are his eyes strange! So in I walk, with a really bad feeling in the pit of my stomach and he sits me down and says:

'Ben, I've been really looking forward to having this chat with you. Would you like a drink and some of my homemade biscuits?'

He pours me some green drink and hands me a biscuit which tastes like nothing I've ever eaten before and we start to talk.

GOODY TWO SHOES – 2

Accompanies text on page 35.

❶ Literal

(a) Select the correct answer.

Jake wouldn't go down to the river because:

(i) he was doing a detention. ☐

(ii) his father wouldn't let him. ☐

(iii) he wanted to help his father. ☐

(iv) he hadn't been there before. ☐

❷ Deductive

(a) Ben was feeling scared because:

(i) he hadn't done his homework. ☐

(ii) something strange had happened to his friends. ☐

(iii) he'd been throwing rocks. ☐

(iv) the dog was barking. ☐

(b) How did Ben know that Jake had changed? _____
_____

❸ Evaluative

(a) What do you think might happen to Ben? _____
_____

(b) Explain why this narrative could be classified as a horror story. _____
_____

(c) Analyse the key elements of the story by completing the diagram.

Genre	Title

Evaluative comment about title

Characters

Setting

Events and action

Prim-Ed Publishing   www.prim-ed.com

Goody two shoes – 3

1 Complete these two profiles of Mr Wizard. The first one is a self-profile and the second is one that Ben may have made about his teacher. You will need to use what you were told about Mr Wizard and the assumptions you made about both characters from the text on page 35. Compare the finished profiles.

Self-profile – Geoffrey Wizard

Appearance

Personality

Likes

Dislikes

Wishes

My teacher – Mr Wizard

Appearance

Personality

Likes

Dislikes

Wishes

Teacher information

Genre:

Informational text – Timetables

Question types and comprehension strategies:

- Analyses and extracts information from a school timetable to answer literal, deductive and evaluative questions.
- Makes connections and compares timetabled information with own experiences.
- Formulates literal, deductive and evaluative questions.

Worksheet information:

- Pupils are asked on page 40 to reflect on the purposes and range of different timetables.
- They should be aware of how accessible information is when presented in this format.
- On page 41, pupils need to formulate literal, deductive and evaluative questions. The icons provided on the questions in the text may aid their understanding of the differences.
- One way of conceptualising these differences is:
  - Literal – the answer is 'right there' in the text.
  - Deductive– the reader is required to 'read and think'.
  - Evaluative – the reader is 'on his/her own' and required to think and make judgments based on personal experiences.

Answers:

Page 40

1. (a) i   (b) iii   (c) French
   (d) Wednesday
2. (a) Monday   (b) (i) English (ii) Teacher check
   (c) Teacher check
3. Teacher check

Page 41

Teacher check

Extension:

- Collect examples of different timetables and list similarities and differences.
- Pupils write descriptive text to provide the same information given in a section of a timetable and compare the two in terms of ease of retrieval and presentation time.

SCHOOL TIMETABLE – 1

Read the school timetable.

School timetable — Class 6H

Time	Monday	Tuesday	Wednesday	Thursday	Friday
8.50 – 9.00	Registration	Registration	Registration	Registration	Registration
9.00 – 10.00	English	English	English	English	Assembly
10.00 – 10.20	Assembly	Assembly	Assembly	Assembly	English
Break					
10.40 – 11.40	Mathematics	Mathematics	Mathematics	Mathematics	Mathematics
11.40 – 12.30	French	Geography	RE	Health	Music
Lunch					
1.30 – 1.45	Reading	Reading	Reading	Reading	Reading
1.45 – 2.45	Science	Art	PE	DT and ICT	History
2.45 – 3.30	Science	Art	PE/Story	DT and ICT	History/Story

SCHOOL TIMETABLE – 2

Use the timetable on page 39 to answer the question.

❶ Literal

Select the correct answer.

(a) On Thursday, the time spent on English is:

    (i) the same as Tuesday. ☐

    (ii) more than Monday. ☐

    (iii) less than Friday. ☐

    (iv) the same as health. ☐

(b) The class has a mathematics lesson:

    (i) before break. ☐

    (ii) after French on Monday. ☐

    (iii) every day. ☐

    (iv) for two hours on Friday. ☐

(c) Which language, other than English, does this class study? _____

(d) On which day does this class have sport? _____

❷ Deductive

(a) On which day would this class be most likely to do a science experiment? _____

(b) (i) Which subject do you think the teacher considers to be the most important? _____

    (ii) Explain why you think this. _____

_____

❸ Evaluative

(a) (i) On which day(s) does your class have sport? _____

    (ii) Which day do you think is the best day to have sport? _____

    (iii) Give reasons. _____

_____

(b) (i) From the timetable, which day would you like the most? _____

    (ii) Explain why. _____

_____

(c) (i) Give three reasons why a teacher would make up a class timetable.

(ii) List other types of timetables.

SCHOOL TIMETABLE – 3

1 Complete this timetable to show what you do in one school day and where each activity takes place. You may need to write more than one activity in some sections.

Time	Activities	Location
0600 to 0700		
0700 to 0800		
0800 to 0900		
0900 to 1000		
1000 to 1100		
1100 to 1200		
1200 to 1300		
1300 to 1400		
1400 to 1500		
1500 to 1600		
1600 to 1700		
1700 to 1800		
1800 to 1900		
1900 to 2000		
2000 to 2100		

2 Timetables should make information more readily available to the reader.

(a) Write five questions for another pupil to answer from the information provided in your timetable. Try to make your questions challenging so that the reader has to read, think and interpret some of your information.

(b) Which question do you think is the most challenging and why?

_____

_____

_____

_____

_____

TWO
LETTERS

Teacher information

Genre:

Letters

Question types and comprehension strategies:

- Analyses and extracts information from two letters to answer literal, deductive and evaluative questions.
- Makes comparisons between the two texts.
- Makes connections between text and character traits.

Worksheet information:

- For the activities on page 45, pupils think specifically about the similarities and differences between the experiences the two main characters, Kathy and Max, are having on the trip. Making comparisons allows readers to obtain a greater understanding of the text.
- Pupils complete sentences describing any personal connections they made to the text. These connections may have occurred due to recognising traits in the characters; having lost a grandparent or parent; or going on holiday with a parent. Effective readers make these connections, gaining a greater understanding of the text.

Answers:

Page 44

1. (i) Yes   (ii) Yes   (iii) No   (iv) Yes
    (v) No   (vi) Yes

2–3. Teacher check

Page 45

Teacher check

Extension:

- Other texts involving letters include:

    Letters to Judy by Judy Blume

    Letters from the inside by John Marsden

    Annushka's voyage by Edith Tarbescu (Picture book)

    Eleanor, Elizabeth by Libby Gleeson

    Flour babies by Anne Fine

TWO LETTERS – 1

Read the two letters, written to the same person.

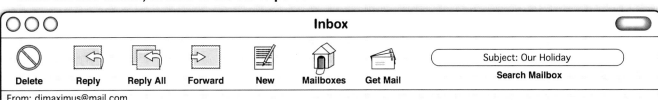

	Inbox						Subject: Our Holiday
Delete	Reply	Reply All	Forward	New	Mailboxes	Get Mail	Search Mailbox

From: djmaximus@mail.com

To: Mike.Corby@mail.com
From: djmaximus@mail.com
Subject: Our Holiday

Hi Dad!

I'm in an Internet cafe in Croydon! It has a coffee shop in it—that's where Mum is (of course!). We caught the bus from right outside Grandad's place.

It was pretty uncomfortable on the plane. Luckily they had computer games and music channels with headphones—otherwise I might have gone a bit crazy from boredom! You were right about the plane food—yuk! They gave me the kids' meals, which was a bit embarrassing. Mine came with mini-chocolate bars though.

Grandad's house is double storey and very skinny. It's in the middle of two other houses and they all look exactly the same. (I'm glad our houses aren't joined together like that, otherwise we'd get lots of complaints from the neighbours about my music!)

Grandad likes wearing ties and he smells like soap. He has LOTS of stamps!! He goes to stamp auctions and buys big bags of them and sorts them. He finds rare ones by using an ultraviolet light to look for invisible marks. He looks like a forensic scientist searching for fingerprints!

Out the back is a cool pond with loads of frogs! There were heaps of tadpoles in the water too and piles of little eggs. Grandad must love his pond! He has three paintings of it in the house—I think Nan painted them.

Tomorrow, Grandad and I are catching the train to London! We are going to go to the Wax Museum, the War Museum and maybe the Science Museum too (hopefully we won't have time for that last one!). We are also going on the London Eye, which is this huge Ferris wheel that looks out over London. I can't wait!

Don't forget to take Mitch for a walk EVERY day, please! Have fun without us!

Max

---

25 March

Dear Mike

How are you? I hope you are not working too hard while we are away. I expect the healthy dinners in the freezer to be eaten by the time we return (and not too many pizza boxes in the rubbish!).

The flight was long and Max played computer games and wore the headphones for most of the trip—leaving me with no-one to talk to! We dragged our luggage onto the busy public transport system and finally arrived at Dad's. I could see immediately that things had changed. The hedges are overgrown and the front garden is in dire need of weeding. Dad looks well but I think he has put on a few kilos. Too many of those cream cakes that Mum used to ban him from. I've warned him about the history of diabetes in our family!

Dad showed Max his stamp collection and his pond. A heavy rain last night brought all the frogs out! It really is a beautiful pond. (Dad is managing to take care of that part of the garden well!) I crept upstairs while they were outside and saw Mum's clothes still hanging in the wardrobe. It took my breath away to see her things sitting just as she had left them on her dresser, too. Poor Dad. Tomorrow, while he takes Max to London for the day, I'll start sorting Mum's things out. I really miss her, Mike, and I wish Max could have met her.

I look forward to seeing you in three weeks. I wish you were here.

Love

Kathy

TWO LETTERS – 2

Use the texts on page 43 to answer the questions.

❶ Literal

(a) Answer yes or no.

   (i) Max enjoys listening to music.   **Yes** **No**

   (iii) Max had met his grandad previously.   **Yes** **No**

   (v) Max is looking forward to going to the science museum.   **Yes** **No**

   (ii) Ultraviolet light shows marks on stamps invisible to the human eye.   **Yes** **No**

   (iv) The rain brought the frogs out.   **Yes** **No**

   (vi) Kathy's mother was a painter.   **Yes** **No**

❷ Deductive

(a) Why do you think Kathy's breath was 'taken away' when she went upstairs?

(b) Why do you think Grandad has been taking such good care of the pond?

(c) Do you think this trip is more than a holiday? What might be its purpose?

_____

_____

_____

❸ Evaluative

(a) How old do you think Max is? _____

(b) What type of person is Kathy?

....
....
....
....
....
....
....

(c) How do you think Grandad is feeling about this visit from his family?

....
....
....
....
....
....
....

TWO LETTERS – 3

Use the texts on page 43 to complete the activities.

1 The characters, Kathy and Max, are on the same trip but are having different experiences. Make comparisons between the two characters' experiences by writing about each of these events.

Event	Max	Kathy
Seeing Grandad's house		
Seeing Grandad		
The pond		
Plans for the next day		

2 When you read a story, your memories of your own experiences, people that you know and the things you have read about or seen in films can be 'triggered'. This is called 'making connections' with the text.

What connections did you make when you read 'Two letters'? Complete the sentences below.

(a) The story reminds me of a time when

(b) The character _____

reminds me of _____

because _____

_____

_____

_____

_____

_____

_____

(c) I think knowing something about _____

helped me to understand the text because _____

_____

_____

_____

_____

HEX AND THE CAPTIVE CITY OF HUR

Teacher information

Genre:

Fairytale

Question types and comprehension strategies:

- Analyses and extracts information from a fairytale to answer literal, deductive and evaluative questions.
- Makes comparisons between a character in a text to himself/herself.
- Makes comparisons between a well-known fairytale and the one given.
- Makes connections between the information in the text and his/her own world.

Worksheet information:

The pupils may be read more difficult or unfamiliar fairytales before completing this activity to reaquaint them with the genre. They may like to retell very familiar fairytales in their own words.

Answers:

Page 48

1. (a) (iii)   (b) (ii)   (c) (i)
2. Teacher check
3. Teacher check

Page 49

Teacher check

Extension:

- The pupils may wish to research and read fairytales from other countries.
- The pupils may like to read titles such as:

    Once upon a more enlightened time by James Finn Garner

    The enchanted forest chronicles by Patricia Wrede

    Book of enchantments by Patricia Wrede

- Read some of Roald Dahl's Revolting Rhymes to the pupils and encourage them to write their own 'fractured' fairytales.

Hex and the captive city of Hur – 1

Read the fairytale.

Once upon a time, in the land of Tech, a cute (but nerdy) computer technician named Hex sat quietly, gaming on his trusted machine.

With his usual finesse and poise, he quickly defeated the villain, Warren the Small, and rescued the doomed city of Marc and its gorgeous queen, Sapira the Gorgeous.

As he began to exit the game, a flash of spiralling lights filled the screen, immediately replaced by the flawless face of Sapira the Gorgeous.

Hex (the cute but nerdy!) stared in shock as she began to speak.

'Because of your heroic deeds (and a score better than anybody else!), you have been chosen to receive three wishes. You may have anything your heart desires, but first you must complete an assignment.'

'Your assignment (should you accept it) is to rescue the isolated city of Hur from the clutches of Nigel the Black. We managed to slip a spy, Torrin the Quick, into the city before contact was lost. Nigel the Black has thrown the elite guards into the dungeon caverns and placed a beast at the entrance to guard them. Defer is a monstrous dog with an enormous appetite and he never sleeps. If you could contact Torrin the Quick, and enlist his help, the elite guards will be able to overtake Nigel's small group of trained warriors and the city will be freed.'

'Sure, Sapira! I can't see any problem! I'll have a go! I have my three wishes all worked out! You can consider the deed done!' replied Hex the cute (but nerdy).

Quickly, he grabbed his mobile phone and scrolled through the numbers he had recorded there. He selected the ones he wanted and dialled. Instantly, he found himself inside the caverns standing next to Torrin the Quick.

'Hey, muscles! I'm Hex and we're about to depart this place!' he confidently stated.

He dialled again and, as if by magic, the pizza delivery person appeared just outside the entrance.

'One barbecue meatlovers for someone named Hex!' he bellowed.

'Over here,' replied Hex, 'right in front of this enormous beast!'

Defer, who had never experienced the delight of a barbecue meatlovers pizza before, gobbled it up as though it was his last meal!

Soothing music (from Hex's portable mp3 player) drifted around the caverns and Defer was lulled into blissful sleep with his stomach full of pizza.

'Well, Torrin! I've done my part. The rest is up to you!' Hex said as he reached for his mobile phone once more, dialled and disappeared from sight.

Torrin the Quick released the elite guards, who overthrew the warriors of Nigel the Black and freed the city of Hur.

Hex lived happily ever after, busily gaming on his custom-built computer with Sapira the Gorgeous at his side and his Mercedes sportscar decorating the driveway.

It just goes to show what technology and a good tip for the pizza delivery boy can achieve!

HEX AND THE CAPTIVE CITY OF HUR – 2

Use the text on page 47 to answer the following questions.

❶ Literal

Underline the best answer for each question.

(a) Why was Hex chosen for the assignment from Queen Sapira?

   (i) *Hex was chosen because he was cute (but nerdy).*

   (ii) *Hex was chosen because he was a great warrior.*

   (iii) *Hex was chosen because he had saved the city of Marc and had a score higher than anyone else.*

(b) What three things did Hex have to do to gain his three wishes?

   (i) He had to fight Nigel the Black, kill Defer the monstrous dog and help the elite guards to defeat the trained warriors of Nigel.

   (ii) He had to contact Torrin the Quick, overcome Defer and allow the elite guards to retake the city from Nigel's warriors.

   (iii) He had to single-handedly defeat Defer, Nigel the Black, and his warriors, to free the city of Hur.

(c) Which words in the text tell you that this is a fairytale?

   (i) 'Once upon a time' and 'lived happily ever after'

   (ii) 'It just goes to show ...'

   (iii) 'Your assignment (should you accept it) ...'

❸ Evaluative

(a) Why does the author use technology as the basis for this modern fairytale?

❷ Deductive

Write full sentence answers for the questions below.

(a) What were the three wishes that Hex made?

_____

_____

_____

_____

_____

_____

(b) Why was Torrin already in the caverns?

_____

_____

_____

_____

_____

_____

(c) How do you know that Hex liked and used all his technological gadgets?

_____

_____

_____

_____

_____

(d) Why are the characters given names such as Nigel the Black, Torrin the Quick, Sapira the Gorgeous, Warren the Small and Hex, the cute (but nerdy)?

_____

_____

_____

_____

_____

_____

HEX AND THE CAPTIVE CITY OF HUR – 3

This page should be used in conjunction with the fairytale on page 47.

1 Complete the chart to compare the main character, Hex, to yourself.

Similarities

Differences

2 Select a familiar fairytale and compare it to the one on page 47 using the categories given.

Familiar fairytale	Hex and the captive city of Hur
Setting	
Characters	
Plot	
Ending	
Language used	

3 Write sentences to compare your leisure pursuits with those of the main character, Hex. If your pursuits are very similar to Hex's, is this a good or bad thing? Why?

_____

_____

_____

_____

_____

THE SECRET BOOK

Teacher information

Genre:

Play

Question types and comprehension strategies:

- Analyses and extracts information from a play to answer literal, deductive and evaluative questions.
- Uses sensory imaging to describe a setting from a character's point of view.

Worksheet information:

For page 53, teachers should ask the pupils to reread the beginning of the play and then close their eyes to help them imagine what the character might see, hear, smell or touch in the tunnel.

Answers:

Page 52

1. (a) (i) She has reached the end of the tunnel.
   - (ii) The trapdoor has suddenly flown open.
   - (iii) He hears a scream.
   - (b) He thinks they have travelled back in time.
2. (a) Teacher check
   - (b) The noise is coming from the peasants who are chasing Jake and Sasha.
   - (c) Teacher check
3. Teacher check

Page 53

Teacher check

Extension:

Look for plays adapted from popular children's books; for example:

Charlie and the chocolate factory by Roald Dahl

Charlotte's web by E B White

Hating Alison Ashley by Robin Klein

The lion, the witch and the wardrobe by C S Lewis

THE SECRET BOOK – 1

Read the play.

Sasha and Jake are brother and sister. One day, they open an old book at their grandmother's house and are suddenly transported to a dirt road, where they are chased by a bunch of angry-looking people. Sasha and Jake make their way into a tunnel into the side of a hill and begin to run in the dim light …

Jake   (*panting*) Sasha! I can hear them. They must be right at the entrance …

Sasha comes to an abrupt halt. Jake crashes into her.

Jake   Hey! Don't stop! They'll find the tunnel any second now.

Sasha feels in her pocket for a torch and switches it on.
The torchlight reveals the end of the tunnel.

Sasha   (*quietly*) We're trapped, Jake.

Shouting and yelling is heard from further up the tunnel.
Jake and Sasha look at each other with fear in their eyes.

Sasha   They can't be far behind us now. Who are they?

Jake   There were pictures of people just like them in that book of Grandma's, remember? It was about people who lived hundreds of years ago.

Sasha   That's impossible, Jake. That would mean we've …

Jake   … travelled back in time.

They fall silent. The noises are growing louder. Jake frantically scrabbles at the walls.

Jake   A tunnel that goes nowhere doesn't make any sense!

Sasha stares at him.

Sasha   You're right, Jake! There has to be a way out of here!

Jake   But the walls are solid. (*He feels above his head.*) And so is the ceiling. (*He whimpers.*) They're going to catch us.

Sasha   Wait. There's one place we haven't tried. (*She shines the torch on the floor of the tunnel and kicks at the ground.*) There's something here.

Sasha drops to her knees and quickly unearths a metal ring.

Jake   It's a trapdoor!

Sasha throws down the torch. They both pull on the ring. The trapdoor flies open, sending them tumbling backwards. Sasha fumbles for the torch and peers into the hole.

Sasha   There's a rope.

Jake   (*peering over her shoulder*) What do you reckon is down there?

The noises are now very loud.

Sasha   I don't know, but it's got to be better than dealing with those crazy people. (*She hands the torch to Jake.*) I'll go first.

Sasha takes a deep breath and lowers herself down the rope. Jake hears a scream. He falls to his knees, peering into the hole.

Jake   Sasha!

THE SECRET BOOK – 2

Use the text on page 51 to answer the questions.

❶ Literal

Answer the questions.

(a) Why:

   (i) *does Sasha come to an abrupt halt?*

   _____

   _____

   _____

   _____

   (ii) *do Jake and Sasha tumble backwards?*

   _____

   _____

   _____

   _____

   (iii) *does Jake fall to his knees and peer into the hole?*

   _____

   _____

   _____

   _____

(b) What does Jake think has happened to him and Sasha?

_____

_____

_____

❷ Deductive

(a) List words that describe how Jake might feel as he says each of these lines.

   (i) 'It's a trapdoor!'

   (ii) 'What do you reckon is down there?'

   (iii) 'They're going to catch us.'

(b) Who is making the noise coming from further down the tunnel?

_____

_____

(c) The noises coming from further down the tunnel are mentioned three times in the play, each time getting louder. Explain what effect this is designed to produce.

_____

_____

_____

_____

_____

_____

❸ Evaluative

Why do you think Sasha screams? Write three possibilities.

THE SECRET BOOK – 3

You are a children's author. You are asked to turn the play excerpt you have just read into a narrative. The first thing you need to do is make the setting more vivid for your readers. You can do this by thinking carefully about what a character might be experiencing through his/her senses.

1 Choose one of the characters from the play.　**J**ake ☐　　**S**asha ☐

2 Focus on the moment the torchlight reveals the end of the tunnel. Now write notes under each heading below. You can use the hints to help you think of more ideas.

> **W**hat can your character see?
>
> Hints: Is the tunnel rocky? Is the light strong or weak? Is the other character's face visible?

> **W**hat can your character hear?
>
> Hints: Is there water dripping? Can he/she hear his/her own breathing?

> **W**hat can your character smell?
>
> Hints: Is the air musty? Are there any animals living in the tunnel?

> **W**hat can your character touch/feel?
>
> Hints: Is the tunnel cold? Is the ground uneven?

3 Use your ideas to describe the setting from your character's point of view.

....

....

....

....

....

....

....

....

....

....

DON'T COUNT YOUR CHICKENS!

Teacher information

Genre:

Fable

Question types and comprehension strategies:

- Analyses and extracts information from fables to answer literal, deductive and evaluative questions.
- Determines the important features of fables and uses these to write his/her own modern fable.

Worksheet information:

Pupils who require extension could write a modern fable with a different moral; e.g. 'Honesty is the best policy', 'A stitch in time saves nine' etc.

Answers:

Page 56

1. (a) Answers will vary, but may include:
   - (i) bucket
   - (ii) bottle, container
   - (iii) stick, pole
   - (iv) murmured, mumbled

   (b) (i) buy some sheep.
   - (ii) The milkmaid tossed her head and … /The pail fell and …
   - (iii) the fox woke up and raced off.
   - (iv) The poor man raised his staff above his head and …

2. (a) Answers will vary, but should indicate that a moral is a type of lesson about life.

   (b) Teacher check

   (c) Teacher check

3. Teacher check

Page 57

Teacher check

Extension:

Find fables on the Internet by typing 'Aesop's fables' into a search engine. Other well-known authors of fables include Phaedrus, Babrius, Bidpai and de France.

Don't count your chickens! – 1

Read the fables.

The milkmaid and her pail (from Ancient Greece – Aesop)

Once there was a milkmaid who began to daydream as she walked to the dairy, carrying a pail of milk on her head.

'The milk in my pail will give me cream, which I'll make into butter and sell at the market', she thought to herself. 'I'll buy some eggs with the money and those will give me chicks. When the chicks have grown, I'll sell some of them. With the money I make, I'll buy myself a beautiful dress. I'll wear this to the fair and all the young men will admire me. But I won't take any notice of them. I'll toss my head and keep walking.'

The milkmaid forgot about the pail of milk and tossed her head. The pail fell to the ground, spilling all the milk.

Moral: *Don't count your chickens before they hatch.*

The boy and the fox (from Sweden)

There once was a village boy who was walking through the forest near his home. He saw a fox lying in a clearing, fast asleep.

'I could kill that fox and sell the skin', the boy muttered to himself. 'With the money I get for it, I'll buy some rye and sow it in my father's field. All the people in the village will see it when they pass by and they'll say "Look at that wonderful rye!". I'll say to them, "Get away from my rye!". But they won't listen. So I'll have to yell, "Get away from my rye!". But they'll still ignore me. So I'll have to run up to them and say it even more loudly.'

The boy became so involved in his ideas that he took a deep breath and screamed, 'GET AWAY FROM MY RYE!'

The noise woke up the fox, who raced off into the forest before the boy even had time to move.

Moral: *It's best to take what you can reach, for of undone deeds you should never screech.*

The poor man and the flask of oil (from India)

Once, a poor man was given a flask of oil by a kind merchant. The poor man put the flask on a shelf and stared at it.

'If I sold that oil, maybe there would be enough to buy some sheep. The sheep would have lambs and soon I would have a large flock. If I sold some of the sheep, I would be rich enough to marry. My wife would have a son and he'd grow to be strong and handsome. But if he was disobedient, I would have to raise my staff to him.'

The man got so carried away that he raised his staff above his head. The staff knocked the flask of oil to the ground, where it broke. The oil was lost.

DON'T COUNT YOUR CHICKENS! – 2

Use the text on page 55 to answer the questions.

❶ Literal

(a) Write another word with a similar meaning for each of these words from the text.

(i) pail _____

(ii) flask _____

(iii) staff _____

(iv) muttered _____

(b) Complete the cause and effect table.

Cause	Effect
(i) *The poor man thought he would sell the oil and …*	
(ii)	*the milk spilt on the ground.*
(iii) *The boy screamed out and …*	
(iv)	*the flask was knocked off the shelf.*

❷ Deductive

(a) A fable is a story that has a moral. What do you think a moral is?

_____

_____

_____

(b) Write a suitable moral for *The poor man and the flask of oil.*

_____

_____

_____

(c) What do the main characters of these fables have in common?

_____

❸ Evaluative

Choose one of the fables and turn it into a cartoon of five or fewer frames. Think carefully about what should go into each frame before you begin.

Title:

DON'T COUNT YOUR CHICKENS! – 3

1 The three fables on page 55 come from three different countries, yet they are similar in many ways. Complete the table for each of the fables.

Title		The boy and the fox	
Setting			
Main character			
Number of characters			
Important object(s)			
Plot	Simple ☐ Complex ☐	Simple ☐ Complex ☐	Simple ☐ Complex ☐
Plot summary			
Moral (in your own words)			

2 List the features you discovered the fables had in common.

....
....
....
....
....
....
....
....
....

3 On a separate sheet of paper, use these common features to help you write a modern version of one of the three fables. Include a modern version of its moral!

IRISH LEGENDS

Teacher information

Genre:

Report

Question types and comprehension strategies:

- Analyses and extracts information from a report to answer literal, deductive and evaluative questions.
- Scans text to locate keywords and phrases to summarise information.
- Determines the importance of information within text by writing a main idea statement.

Worksheet information:

Before completing the activity on page 61, pupils could highlight keywords and phrases in the text on page 59 to help them complete the table and explain the main idea for each legend. Pupils could compare their statements and determine those which accurately described the main idea.

Answers:

Page 60

1. (a) (iii)   (b) (ii)   (c) (iv)
2. (a) Teacher check
   (b) The part of the word Irish word for fairy in bold print ('**sidhe**og') means hillocks or mounds where fairies are said to inhabit.
   (c) Teacher check
   (d) Teacher check
3. Teacher check

Page 61

Teacher check

Extension:

- Pupils can report on two other Irish legends; the 'wearing of the green' and the Claddagh Ring.
- If pupils are interested in Irish legends and mythology, the much-loved Irish fairytale, *The children of Lir*, can be found on page 23.

IRISH LEGENDS – 1

Read the report about Irish legends.

A legend is a story with its origin based on an actual event in the past.

Irish fairy folk

The Irish word for fairy is 'sidheog' (pronounced 'sheehog'). Fairies, it is believed, live in hillocks or mounds ('sidhe') and it is said that touching or disturbing them will bring bad luck. Their origin goes back to the time Ireland was ruled by the highly regarded Tuatha de Dannan, an intelligent race of people who many considered to have magical powers or even to be gods. However, after battles against invading forces over a period of 200 years, the Tuatha were eventually defeated by the Milesians. The Milesians allowed the Tuatha to remain in Ireland, but only if they lived underground ... and so began the legend of the fairy folk.

The leprechaun

The most well-known Irish fairy is the leprechaun. According to legend, he looks like a tiny old man, wears a green tunic with a green hat, can be found sitting under a tree mending fairies' shoes and possesses a hidden pot of gold. It is said if you catch a leprechaun he will lead you to his pot of gold—but only if you don't take your eyes off him! Otherwise, he will vanish into thin air.

The banshee

A banshee is a type of female fairy woman. She has long flowing silver-grey hair and wears a long grey-white cloak over her thin body. Her skin is pale and her eyes are red from continual crying. This is because it is believed she cries and wails outside the houses of those who have someone within who is about to die. The wailing sound is a dreaded warning.

St Patrick

St Patrick is the patron saint of Ireland. Around 430 AD, Patrick went to Ireland to spread the Christian religion. (Today, over 93 per cent of Ireland's population are Catholic.)

There are several legends associated with St Patrick, probably the most well-known being the story that, with God's help, he drove all the venomous snakes in Ireland into the sea, where they drowned. To this day, there are no venomous snakes in Ireland.

The Blarney Stone

The Blarney Stone is set in a wall of Blarney Castle, located in the Irish village of the same name. Kissing the stone is said to give the kisser 'the Irish gift of the Blarney', which is the ability to speak eloquently and persuasively but in such a manner that it is not offensive. One legend claims that the stone's powers came from an old woman who rewarded a king of the castle who saved her from drowning.

To kiss the stone, you have to lie on your back and bend backwards and downwards, holding on to iron bars for support!

The Irish shamrock

The name 'shamrock' comes from an Irish word meaning 'three-leaved'. According to legend, St Patrick used the plant, a common clover, to help explain the meaning of the Holy Trinity (Father, Son and Holy Spirit as one Being) to his followers. The shamrock is the national flower of Ireland and its most famous symbol.

IRISH LEGENDS – 2

Use the text on page 59 to answer the questions.

❶ Literal

Circle the best answer.

(a) The legend of the Irish fairy folk began with ...

   (i) *the Irish* ☐

   (ii) *the Milesians* ☐

   (iii) *the Tuatha de Dannan* ☐

(b) A leprechaun looks like ...

   (i) *a small man* ☐

   (ii) *a tiny old man* ☐

   (iii) *a small old man* ☐

(c) A banshee has ...

   (i) *silver-grey hair, dark skin, red eyes* ☐

   (ii) *silver-grey hair, pale skin, blue eyes* ☐

   (iii) *grey hair, pale skin, red eyes* ☐

   (iv) *silver-grey hair, red eyes, pale skin* ☐

❷ Deductive

(a) According to legend, why are there no venomous snakes in Ireland?

(b) Why do you think the Irish word for fairy is 'sidheog'?

(c) Thousands of tourists a year visit Blarney Castle to kiss the stone. Why do you think this is?

(d) Why do you think the shamrock was chosen as Ireland's national flower?

❸ Evaluative

(a) There have been no reports of finding a leprechaun's pot of gold. Why do you think this is so?

_____

_____

_____

(b) How do you think the legend of the banshee might have begun?

_____

_____

(c) Would you visit Blarney Castle and kiss the Blarney Stone? Explain your answer.

IRISH LEGENDS – 3

Use the text on page 59 to complete the activity.

1 (a) Scan the text to find keywords and phrases. Write these next to each legend to summarise the information.

(b) Use the information you recorded to describe the main idea for each legend.

Legend	Keywords and phrases	Main idea
Irish fairy folk		
The leprechaun		
The banshee		
St Patrick		
The Blarney Stone		
The shamrock		

Genre:

Biography

Question types and comprehension strategies:

- Analyses and extracts information from a biography to answer literal, deductive and evaluative questions.
- Discriminates between important and less important information contained in a text.
- Identifies key information contained in a text to write a summary.

Worksheet information:

- Discriminating between important and less important information contained in a text is a vital skill for pupils to gain, especially for their secondary and tertiary education. Pupils need to practise the strategy of stripping away extraneous information from a text to summarise the main idea. Discuss with the class that the summarising paragraph needs to give the reader the main idea of who Layne Beachley is and what she has achieved.

Answers:

Page 64

1. (a) (i) Fact   (ii) Fact   (iii) Opinion
        (iv) Fact   (v) Opinion

2–3. Teacher check

Page 65

Teacher check

Extension:

Look at the biographies of other elite surfers on the Internet, using a search engine such as 'google'.

- Kelly Slater
- Mark Occhilupo
- Taj Burrows
- Yvonne Byron
- Stephanie Gilmore (Roxy-pro champion of 2005)

A SURFING CHAMPION – 1

Read the biography.

Name:	*Layne Beachley*
Nickname:	*'Gidget' or 'Beach'*
Born:	*Sydney, Australia*
Birth date:	*24 May 1972*
Lives:	*Northshore Hawaii/Sydney Australia*
Turned professional:	*16 years old*
Accomplishments:	*Six consecutive World Titles*
Trademark moves:	*Big wave riding*

Layne was adopted by Neil and Valerie Beachley at six weeks old. At the age of four, Layne's dad gave her a surfboard. She had already been skateboarding for a year prior to this, and soon discovered she was good at surfing too.

Growing up in Sydney, Australia, Layne played football and tennis and would ride her bicycle to Manly Beach to teach herself to surf. While in Year 10 at school, Layne entered and won the regional scholastic surfing title. She was placed among the state of New South Wales' best schoolgirl surfers. She went on to win competitions and was placed fifth in the nationals. By the time Layne was 16, her talent and determination found her competing in professional surfing competitions around Australia.

Layne completed her High School Certificate and for the next four years worked up to four part-time jobs a week to save the money needed to finance her surfing ambition and to be able to compete overseas.

By 20, Layne was ranked number 6 in the world. She started vigorous fitness and strength training that would give her the edge over other women surfers. She continued winning competitions and discovered success in the 'big wave' events. Layne would challenge nine-metre waves—the height of a three storey building—and conquer them! Layne celebrated her 21st birthday and claimed her first World Tour victory.

In 1993 and 1996, Layne was struck down with Chronic Fatigue Syndrome. She worked hard, listening to her body, trying to determine what gave her the physical and mental energy to get out of bed each day. Although Layne considered giving up surfing, she persevered and overcame the disease each time.

By 1998 Layne had won five out of the 11 World Championship Events. She was a major competitor, earning the most prize money a women surfer had ever earnt in one single season.

Layne continued to dominate the women's surfing circuit. To date, she has won six consecutive World Championships from 1998 to 2003, a feat never achieved before by any surfer, male or female.

One of Layne's goals has always been to promote women's surfing and to encourage girls to pursue their dreams whether they have sporting, cultural or academic goals. In 1993, Layne created the 'Aim for the Stars Foundation' that offers financial grants and support to girls with big dreams.

Layne also runs surfing clinics and speaks publicly to young people. In 2003, Layne joined UNICEF, helping the organisation raise awareness of the need for safe drinking water around the globe. In 2004, Layne Beachley was awarded the Australian Female Athlete of the Year.

In March, 2005, at age 32, Layne was the runner-up at the Margaret River Masters, in Perth, Western Australia. Layne's 16-year career on the professional women's surfing scene continues.

Use the text on page 63 to answer the questions.

❶ Literal

(a) Decide if the statements are fact or opinion.

   (i) Layne began skateboarding at the age of three.

     Fact **Opinion**

   (ii) By 16, Layne was surfing in national competitions.

     Fact **Opinion**

   (iii) Layne prefers the big-wave events because there is less competition.

     Fact **Opinion**

   (iv) In 1998, Layne earnt more prize money than any other female surfer in one season.

     Fact **Opinion**

   (v) Layne believes that young people can achieve anything if they work hard enough.

     Fact **Opinion**

❸ Evaluative

(a) Layne Beachley is considered to be a role model for young people. Do you agree? Explain your answer.

❷ Deductive

(a) How are people with Chronic Fatigue Syndrome affected?

(b) How does Layne Beachley use her profile and success to benefit others?

(c) Is Layne Beachley Australia's most successful surfer?

(d) Which personal traits does Layne possess, enabling her to achieve such great success in her life?

(e) What factors in Layne's own life do you think inspired her to create the 'Aim for the Stars Foundation'?

(f) How do you think Layne overcoming Chronic Fatigue Syndrome affected her future career?

A SURFING CHAMPION – 3

Use the text on page 63 to complete the activities.

Being able to identify keywords and phrases in a text and then summarise that information are important skills to learn—and they take practice!

You are going to condense the biography about Layne Beachley into one paragraph of information.

1 Reread the text. Underline keywords and phrases.

2 Sort the words and phrases you have underlined by placing them in one of the following categories. Use point form to record the information.

The main idea(s)	Other important facts	Incidental (less important) facts

3 Use the information above to write one paragraph that summarises the life of Layne Beachley.

....

....

....

....

....

....

....

....

....

....

BARE TREES BAFFLE LOCAL FARMER

Teacher information

Genre:

Journalistic writing – newspaper report

Question types and comprehension strategies:

- Analyses and extracts information from a journalistic report to answer literal, deductive and evaluative questions.
- Scans text to locate words and to find contextual information to assist in determining meaning.
- Paraphrases understanding of a word meaning before writing it and consulting a dictionary.

Worksheet information:

- The journalistic report uses some challenging vocabulary which is the focus of the activity on page 69. Pupils should be encouraged to select less familiar words to include in their word charts or the words can, alternatively, be teacher selected.
- Pupils will consult a dictionary and write another definition to complement or correct their definition.

Answers:

Page 68

1. (a) (i) false (ii) false (iii) true (iv) true
   (v) false (vi) false (vii) true

2–3. Teacher check

Page 69

Teacher check

Extension:

- Collect newspaper reports and sort them into categories; e.g. sports, business, human interest stories, crime, social events. Discuss similarities and differences.
- Discuss the importance of headlines and headers, what they aim to do and what makes them successful or unsuccessful.

BARE TREES BAFFLE LOCAL FARMER – 1

Read the journalistic report.

Bare trees baffle local farmer

A most unusual and it would appear inexplicable phenomenon is causing concern to the small community of Cosgrove.

Last Friday, local farmer James Wilson observed that a clump of approximately 12 trees growing in the south-east corner of his property were totally denuded of foliage and covered with a strange, white, sticky substance. The concerned farmer was even more amazed to discover a circle of brown, burnt earth nearby—and that there wasn't a leaf to be seen on the ground.

Fearing some exotic disease and the possibility of it spreading and infecting other plants, he contacted the Forestry Department, who visited the site and declared that the trees were healthy and disease-free. On their advice, he then contacted the Agriculture Department to ensure that the problem wasn't the result of an insect plague. They were unable to find anything to suggest that this was the case.

Local interest is growing and wild and varied theories and explanations are being discussed. Locals, wishing to see for themselves, are visiting the site in droves, looking for evidence of alien spaceships, human intervention or some natural phenomenon. There seems to be little evidence to support any of their theories to date.

As the mystery deepens, visitors from further afield are also descending on this previously quiet rural retreat. Local businesses are booming as they struggle to provide sufficient accommodation, food and services for the hordes of urban invaders.

James Wison is not enjoying his notoriety. He is refusing to answer his telephone. The gate at the end of the track leading to his farmhouse has a huge padlock on it and prominently displays a large sign with the very clear message that visitors are unwelcome. Undeterred, curious members of the press and the general public are ignoring his attempts to discourage their unwanted attention and are swarming across all barriers to inspect the site for themselves. Mr Wilson now has to contend with rounding up stray stock that has wandered off because gates have been left open, extinguishing small fires lit by campers, repairing fences and collecting a multitude of bottles, cans and other rubbish discarded by inconsiderate, unwelcome visitors.

Last night Mr Wilson appeared on a regional television programme and said that '… there was nothing to see' and that he just wanted his quiet life back. He added that he regretted that he had ever '… opened his big mouth', that it was all '… a big fuss about nothing' and that he wished it would all '… just go away'.

Local police have appealed to the public to come forward with any reliable information that could help to explain the mystery or lead to the apprehension of any person or persons responsible. Otherwise, they should respect Mr Wilson's request for privacy and refrain from trespassing on his property. Police further warned that any future trespassers would be prosecuted. They intend to erect signs to this effect and to provide regular patrols to ensure compliance.

Farmer James Wilson surveys his mystery trees

BARE TREES BAFFLE LOCAL FARMER – 2

Answer the questions using the text on page 67.

❶ Literal

(a) Answer true or false.

(i) There was a circle of brown earth around the trees.

[True] [False]

(ii) James Wilson enjoyed the publicity.

[True] [False]

(iii) The Forestry Department recommended that the farmer should contact the Agriculture Department.

[True] [False]

(iv) The visitors ignored Mr Wilson's sign.

[True] [False]

(v) The visitors took care of Mr Wilson's property.

[True] [False]

(vi) Mr Wilson appeared on television because he wanted to publicise what had happened on his farm.

[True] [False]

(vii) The police believe that it is possible that someone may have caused the damage to the trees.

[True] [False]

❷ Deductive

(a) Who do you think broke Farmer Wilson's fences and why?

(b) Do you think that the local people were happy about the publicity their district was attracting?

[Yes] [No]

Explain why you think this. _____

_____

_____

_____

(c) Were the police justified in taking the action they did?

[Yes] [No]

Why/not? _____

_____

_____

_____

❸ Evaluative

(a) Do you think people will take any notice of the signs the police are going to erect?   [Yes] [No]

Give reasons for your answer. _____

_____

_____

(b) What do you think will happen next at Cosgrove?

(c) What do you think could have caused the mysterious phenomenon?

BARE TREES BAFFLE LOCAL FARMER – 3

Complete the chart of interesting words from the text on page 67.

- Select and write 6 words that you find interesting.
- Write your definition of the word meaning.
- Identify the paragraph where the word is used.
- Consult a dictionary, then write a dictionary definition.
- Read the sentence for help with a possible meaning.

Word	Paragraph	My definition	Dictionary definition

MIRROR IMAGE

Genre:

Science fiction

Question types and comprehension strategies:

- Analyses and extracts information from a science fiction text to answer literal, deductive and evaluative questions.
- Scans a science fiction text to locate specific information.
- Synthesises information to compare characters from a text and to complete arguments for and against a debate.

Worksheet information:

- Teachers should exercise care and sensitivity when completing page 72 as it deals with adoption and may affect some pupils in the class.
- Page 73 (Question 1) expects pupils to show comprehension of the text on page 71 by completing a character portrait in words and illustrations. Question 2 requires pupils to use the examples from the text and their own background knowledge to plan bullet points for arguments for and against the heredity vs environment issue.

Answers:

Page 72

1. (a) (ii) His school was having its orientation day at secondary school.

   (b) (i) He wore clothes and did his hair differently from the other pupils in his group.

2. Teacher check

3. Teacher check

Page 73

Teacher check

Extension:

Pupils may enjoy reading these science fiction titles, some of which relate to the topic of adoption, increasing the numbers of endangered species and family relationships:

The angel factory by Terence Blacker

The exchange pupil by Kate Gilmore

Earthborn by Sylvia Waugh

Space race by Sylvia Waugh

MIRROR IMAGE – 1

Read the science fiction story.

David Roberts knew that he was different from other twelve-year-olds.

His parents had often told him that he had been specially chosen from a number of eggs and created just to be their 'special' child. His hair and eye colour resembled that of his adoptive parents, Marion and Jeff Roberts. He was slightly built like his dad, who was wiry like a runner, but he had his mum's determination and stubbornness. His parents encouraged and supported him in whatever he wanted to do. He knew that he was well loved.

The day came for David's secondary school orientation. He was to visit the local secondary school with his primary school classmates so that the following year everything would not be so strange and overwhelming. Other local schools were also going to be present on the same day.

As the different school groups passed on their tour, the pupils critically assessed each other. They wondered if any of the pupils would be in their classes next year, whether they would become friends or enemies and who were the 'cool' kids in each group.

David noticed a particular boy in one of the groups because he was being very closely supervised by a male teacher. The teacher addressed the boy as 'Slade' whenever he needed to move the group along to the next venue. Slade was slightly built with brown hair, dark skin and brown eyes. However, his clothes were not as dull as those of the other pupils —he was the only pupil who wore an expensive denim jacket. He had taken a lot of time to spike his hair with gel. The sturdy army boots he wore were scuffed from constant use. He strutted along in his unusual garb as though he was wearing a badge of honour, completely oblivious to the teacher at his side and the stares and comments from pupils in other groups.

As the groups settled down for a lunch break, David noticed that Slade was sitting slightly apart from the other pupils in his group but closer to David's group. David talked to his friends as he demolished his lunch. During a lull in conversation, David looked around at the unfamiliar faces of pupils he would be attending secondary school with the following year. His eyes encountered Slade, who had turned to look around at the other pupils. Their eyes met and held. Each found himself spellbound by the apparition staring back.

David's hair was fair, but Slade's was dark. David's skin was fair but Slade's was dark. David's eyes were blue, but Slade's were brown. The strange thing was that the facial features were exactly the same. It was almost like looking at a mirror image which had been reversed on a photocopier or a negative film image.

David pulled himself free from his semi-catatonic state and spoke to Slade.

'You're ... You're just like me. You could be my twin!' stammered David.

'Yeah!', replied Slade. 'Spooky! Strange! My mum always told me I was a little different — created just to be their 'special' child. Like I would believe garbage like that!'

As David related the events of the day to his parents, he watched as a thoughtful expression came across his mother's face.

'Do you know, I recall Dr Lewitt talking about his special interest in genetic engineering whenever I went for my tests', she said.

MIRROR IMAGE – 2

Use the text on page 71 to answer the questions.

Use the text on page 71 to answer the questions.

❶ Literal

Tick the correct answer for the question.

(a) Why was David at the secondary school?

    (i) *His school was attending a live stage performance with other schools.* ☐

    (ii) *His school was having its orientation day at secondary school.* ☐

    (iii) *He was competing in an interschool competition at the secondary school grounds.* ☐

(b) Why did Slade stand out among the pupils in his group?

    (i) *He wore different clothes and did his hair differently from the pupils in his group.* ☐

    (ii) *He was taller and better looking than the other pupils.* ☐

    (iii) *His parents could not afford to dress him properly.* ☐

❷ Deductive

(a) Write full sentence answers to answer the questions below.

    (i) Why did Slade want his appearance to stand out among the other pupils?

_____

_____

_____

_____

_____

_____

_____

_____

    (ii) Do you think that Slade's parents cared for him as much as David's parents? Find words in the text to support your opinion.

_____

_____

_____

_____

_____

_____

_____

_____

    (iii) How do you think that David felt when he saw someone who looked almost exactly like him? Use words from the text to support your answer.

_____

_____

_____

_____

_____

_____

_____

❸ Evaluative

(a) Why do you think that children, adopted or otherwise, even within one family, can be so different from each other?

Primary comprehension   Prim-Ed Publishing   www.prim-ed.com

MIRROR IMAGE – 3

This page relates the text on page 71.

1 In the boxes below, write descriptions and draw illustrations to match the two boys in the text. Include aspects of their personalities and behaviour.

David

Slade

There have been many arguments and debates about how much influence parents' genetic characteristics (heredity) have on an individual's character, compared to the environment in which he/she is brought up.

2 Use the information gained from the examples in the text and your own knowledge to write arguments (in bullet form) for and against the following:

Environment creates most aspects of an individual's character.

For

....
....
....
....
....
....
....
....
....
....
....

Against

....
....
....
....
....
....
....
....
....
....
....

LIFE OF A CONVICT

Teacher information

Genre:

Autobiography

Question types and comprehension strategies:

- Analyses and extracts information from an autobiography to answer literal, deductive and evaluative questions.
- Uses synthesis to consider, compare and analyse the effects of a major event in a writer's life.

Worksheet information:

Before the pupils begin the activity on page 77, teachers may like to give some more examples of how life events can be seen in a positive and negative light, emphasising the positive.

Answers:

Page 76

1. (a) (i) opinion   (ii) fact
   (iii) fact   (iv) opinion

   (b) 1826   he was born

   1835   his mother died

   1839   he was caught picking pockets, he was sentenced to transportation or he was sent to Van Diemen's Land/ Point Puer

   1846   he married Mary Clifton

2. (a) Answers should indicate that it was a major event in his life so far.

   (b) Teacher check

3. Teacher check

Page 77

Teacher check

Extension:

Find autobiographies of the pupils' favourite authors on the Internet.

LIFE OF A CONVICT – 1

Read the autobiography.

I was born in London, England in 1826. My life as a young child was extremely unhappy. My mother was the only member of my family I knew and she died when I was nine years old. I then lived on the streets and had to steal so I could live. When I was 13 years old, I was caught picking pockets.

I thought I would be sent straight to prison, but instead I was sentenced to transportation. This meant that I would have to take a long sea voyage to a place called Van Diemen's Land—now known as Tasmania. Although I was frightened by this, I couldn't help feeling faintly hopeful. At least I wouldn't be on the streets any more. Nothing could be worse than that. Or could it?

With hundreds of other convicts, I spent about five months on the ship that travelled to Australia. I was miserable – it was cramped, dirty and uncomfortable and I was seasick a lot of the time. When we arrived in Van Diemen's Land, I was taken to a place called Point Puer. This was a prison for boys aged between 9 and 17. It was across the bay from the men's prison called Port Arthur and consisted of a group of dilapidated buildings.

Soon after I arrived, I was assigned to a labouring gang, which meant physical work like cutting firewood and making bricks. After a few months, I was among a group of boys who were chosen to learn trades. My chosen trade was shoemaking. To my surprise, I quite enjoyed it. What I didn't enjoy was the harsh conditions at Point Puer. Life was an endless cycle of prayers, church, work and school. The only real free time we had was on Saturday afternoons. There was also the constant threat of punishment. Any boy who misbehaved could suffer solitary confinement, reduced rations or beatings. Not long after I arrived at Point Puer, I spent 10 days in solitary confinement for fighting with another boy. It was so terrifying that from then on I was mostly well-behaved. However, like many of the other boys, I stole food and tools to trade with the men who arrived each day from Port Arthur to bring us water and food. I was never caught, although some of the other boys were.

Finally, after two years at Point Puer, I was given my ticket-of-leave. I went to live in nearby Hobart and soon found work with a shoemaker. When I was 20, I married a young woman named Mary Clifton and we had a son called Matthew. Life became much better. I eventually bought my own shoe shop.

I now have a happy life living in Hobart. I have no wish to go back to England. Matthew doesn't know about my former life yet, but one day I plan to tell him. He is now exactly the same age I was when I left England. I know that his life will be better than mine.

LIFE OF A CONVICT – 2

Accompanies text on page 75.

❶ Literal

(a) Tick fact or opinion for each of these statements.

(i) The writer was a good pickpocket.

Fact **Opinion**

(ii) Tasmania was once called Van Diemen's Land.

Fact **Opinion**

(iii) The writer thought that life in Australia might better than life in London.

Fact **Opinion**

(iv) Working for a shoemaker in Hobart was an excellent opportunity for the writer.

Fact **Opinion**

(b) Write an event that took place in the writer's life for each date in the time line.

1826

1835

1839

1846

❷ Deductive

(a) Why do you think that most of the writer's autobiography is about his time in Point Puer?

_____

_____

_____

(b) List three possible reasons why the writer may not want to go back to London again.

❸ Evaluative

(a) Imagine you are Matthew. Your father has just told you about his convict life for the first time. Write what your response might be. Include any questions you have for him.

(b) Do you think the boys at Point Puer should have been allowed more free time?

Yes **No**

Give reasons to support your answer.

_____

_____

_____

_____

LIFE OF A CONVICT – 3

Most events in our lives have positive and negative aspects. For example, failing a test might be negative because you have to do the test again, but also positive because it helps you to understand what areas you need to work on.

1 Using the text from page 75, think about the writer's experience of going to Point Puer for two years. List the main effects you think this might have had on his life. They can be positive or negative.

2 Write a 'P' next to each positive effect and an 'N' next to each negative effect.

3 Mark the scale to show your view of the overall effect of Point Puer on the writer's life.

Positive   **Negative**

4 Based on your answers, write a short speech from the writer's point of view, explaining how Point Puer affected your life. Indicate if it had more positive or negative effects.

5 Deliver your speech to a partner and then listen to his/hers. List some of the differences.

Genre:

Poetry

Question types and comprehension strategies:

- Analyses and extracts information from two poems to answer literal, deductive and evaluative questions.
- Uses summarising and paraphrasing to show comprehension of two poems.

Worksheet information:

- The poems given are forms of poetry called 'kennings'. A kenning is a literacy device where a new noun or noun phrase is created to replace a more familiar noun. It helps the reader or poet to think more carefully about how to describe, in shortened form, an ordinary object in an extraordinary way. It was commonly used in Anglo-Saxon poetry.

Answers:

Pages 79–80

1. (a) (i) Yes   (ii) No   (iii) Yes   (iv) Yes
2. Teacher check
3. Teacher check

Page 81

Teacher check

Extension:

- Pupils may wish to investigate examples of kennings found on the Internet in stories such as the story of Beowulf or used in book or film titles such as *Whale rider* and *The bone collector*.
- Another more unusual form of poetry is the 'tanka' which is similar to haiku. Pupils may enjoy researching and writing both of these forms as well as some kennings of their own.

MY BASS GUITAR AND MY COMPUTER – 1

Read the poems below, which are written in a poetic form called *kennings*.

My computer is ...

Word processor, information researcher,

game player, layout organiser,

design creator, email dispenser,

comrade communicator,

email receiver, knowledge gatherer,

shopping provider, technology utiliser,

telephone interrupter, buddy networker,

data storer, program runner,

information presenter, homework helper,

image manipulator, music downloader,

parent confuser, up-grade collector,

energy user, virus attractor,

human contact inhibitor!

My bass guitar is ...

Melody maker, rhythm keeper,

chord changer, string strummer,

beat bellower, song accompanier,

sound echoer, vibration boomer,

noise maker, finger flicker,

hand mover, arm placer,

head banger, leg knocker,

neck stretcher, palm painer,

air stirrer, floor shaker,

parent annoyer, peer satisfier,

crowd pleaser, mood lifter,

listener attracter, ego expander,

babe attractor!

❶ Literal

(a) Tick yes/no to show whether the statement is true or not.

(i) A bass guitar can keep rhythm and beat and accompany a song.

| Yes | No |

(ii) Playing the guitar can cause calluses to form on your fingertips.

| Yes | No |

(iii) Computers can be networked.

| Yes | No |

(iv) There are some advantages and disadvantages to using computers.

| Yes | No |

❷ Deductive

(a) Write some words from the poems which show that:

(i) Bass guitars are not popular with everyone.

(ii) Playing the bass guitar can build the player's self-esteem and confidence.

(iii) Some people have difficulty using computers.

(iv) Computers can be expensive to own and use.

Mᴀʏ BASS GUITAR AND MY COMPUTER – 2

Use the text on page 79 to answer the questions.

Use the text on page 79 to answer the questions.

❸ Evaluative

(a) Write sentences to answer the following questions, making sure that you give reasons or explanations.

(i) How can learning to play a musical instrument help a person's health and wellbeing?

(ii) Is today's society too dependent upon computers?

_____

_____

_____

_____

(iii) Has the invention of devices such as the computer and the bass guitar made it more difficult for people to get along with each other?

_____

_____

_____

_____

(b) Use the boxes below to record keywords from the poems about bass guitars and computers.

Bass guitars	**C**omputers

Primary comprehension

Prim-Ed Publishing   www.prim-ed.com

MY BASS GUITAR AND MY COMPUTER – 3

1 Complete the table using information from the text on page 79.

Bass guitars		Computers	
Advantages	*Disadvantages*	*Advantages*	*Disadvantages*

2 Write paragraphs to summarise the main information given by the poet about bass guitars and computers.

(a) **Bass guitars:**

....
....
....
....
....
....
....
....
....
....
....
....
....
....

(b) **Computers:**

....
....
....
....
....
....
....
....
....
....
....
....
....
....